QUICK REVIEW
IN
INORGANIC CHEMISTRY

M.S. Yadav

ANMOL PUBLICATIONS PVT. LTD.
NEW DELHI - 110 002 (INDIA)

ANMOL PUBLICATIONS PVT. LTD.
4374/4B, Ansari Road, Daryaganj
New Delhi - 110 002
Ph.: 23261597, 23278000
Visit us at: www.anmolpublications.com

Quick Review in Inorganic Chemistry
© Author

First Published, 2004

PRINTED IN INDIA

Published by J.L. Kumar for Anmol Publications Pvt. Ltd., New Delhi - 110 002 and Printed at Mehra Offset Press, Delhi.

Contents

Contents

Preface

Inorganic chemistry is the branch of chemistry in which all the known elements (except carbon) and their compounds are studied. It is therefore a descriptive study. An attempt has been made in this book to present the subject matter in a unified manner. The main emphasis is to understand various elements on the basis of their position in the long form of periodic table. The topics included in (this book are those which are prescribed in) the syllabus for degree classes by the Indian Universities. A concise account of each topic has been given and an effort has been made to explain the behaviour as the basis of electronic configurations and gradation in properties down a group or across a period of the periodic table.

It has been assumed that students are already familiar with the important properties of elements. The classification of elements as **metals** and **non-metals**, as **representative elements** and **transition elements**, and **lanthanides** and **actinides** etc. They are also familiar with reducing and oxidizing nature of elements and other such properties as magnetic behaviour of the elements. These have been taken up in various chapters to explain the chemistry of elements.

A conscious effort has been made to avoid the use of mathematics and only a minimum use has been made where it was unavoidable to clear a point.

I have taken help from a number of books, available, to prepare the manuscript and are thankful to all such authors and publishers for this.

The book is expected to serve as a textbook, reference book for the students of chemistry in degree classes of the Indian Universities.

I am to thank M/s Anmol Publications for bringing out the book in such a good form and in such a short time.

Author Name

1

Atomic Structure

1.1 Nuclear Atom and Radioactivity

Atom. It is the smallest particle of an element that takes part in a chemical reaction. It may or may not be capable of independent existence. John Dalton considered atoms as structureless indivisible particles.

The inner structure of atom was proposed by Rutherford and he considered atom as made up of a positive centre called nucleus (of the size of 10^{-15} m) which contains *neutrons* and *protons*, and *electrons* revolve round the nucleus in circular paths (orbits). The radius of an atom is of the order of 10^{-10} m.

Electron exhibits both *particle nature* and *wave nature*.

Particle Nature. A particle occupies a *definite* position in space and the same position cannot be occupied simultaneously by any other particle *i.e.* the *particle is localised* in space.

Wave Nature. A wave is spread out in space. A number of waves can exist in same space simultaneously *i.e.* a *wave is delocalised* in space.

Nucleus. It is that portion of the atom which contains protons and neutrons (*i.e. nucleous*). It is positively charged and the negatively charged electrons are attracted to the nucleus by the **electrostatic forces** of attraction.

Chemical bonding between atoms alters the motion of electrons, the nuclei remaining unchanged. Nuclei retains the 'chemical identity' and the occurrence of chemical elements depends on existence of stable nuclei.

Atomic Sizes are determined by the radii of the electronic orbits.

Atomic Number (Z) of an element is equal to the number of protons in its nucleus. In a neutral atom the number of protons is the same as the number of electrons.

Mass Number (A): It is equal to the sum of protons and neutrons present in the nucleus of an atom. The protons and neutrons are collectively known as **nucleous**.

Protons and neutrons are held together by an attractive force of *extremely short range*, known as **strong interaction**. It opposes the long range electrostatic repulsion between protons. The balance of these two opposing forces determines the stability of the atom.

For stability of n/p of an atom should be around 1.

The **quantum theory** can be used to explain the stability and structure of an atom.

Quantum Theory. According to it

(i) The energy is radiated or absorbed by a body not continuously but discontinuously in the form of small packets **(quantum)**.

(ii) The energy of quantum is directly proportional to the frequency of radiation ($E = h\nu$).

It has been observed that nuclei with even number of either protons or neutrons (or both are more stable than the atoms with odd numbers.

The **magic numbers** (8, 20, 28, 50, 82, 126) of protons or neutrons give extra stability to the atoms *e.g.* ^{16}O, ^{208}Pb which have magic number of both protons and neutrons.

Isotopes. Nuclei with same number of protons but different number of **nucleons** (proton + neutron) are called **isotopes** *e.g.* $^{1}_{1}H$ and $^{2}_{1}H$; $^{16}_{8}O$ and $^{17}_{18}O$ etc.

Isotones. Nuclei with same number of neutrons but different number of nucleus are called **isotones.**

Isobars. Nuclei with same number of nucleons but different number of protons are called **isobars**.

Isodiapheres. Atoms of different elements having same difference in number of neutrons and number of protons (N – P same) are known as **Isodiapheres** *e.g.* $^{233}_{92}U$ and $^{231}_{90}Th$. In both case (N – P) = 51.

Isotopic number. It is the difference in number of neutrons and protons in the nucleus.

Isotopic number = Mass number – 2 × atomic number.

Isosters. Two or more molecules having same number of atoms and same number of electrons are known as isosters *e.g.* N_2O, CO_2.

Radioactivity. The spontaneous emission of radiations by an element or its compound is called **radioactivity.**

Natural radioactivity. The spontaneous disintegration of the nuclei of certain naturally occurring elements like uranium, thorium, polonium, radium etc. is known as natural radioactivity.

Artificial radioactivity. The spontaneous emission of radiations by many man-made elements, which are radioactive is called **artificial radioactivity.**

Radioactive elements are those elements which show property of radioactivity.

Alpha rays (α-rays). Such rays are made up of helium atoms that have lost two electrons (*i.e.* He^{2+}) and are represented as ^4_2He. These rays carry positive charge and so are deflected strongly by an electrostatic field. They can penetrate through an aluminium sheet 0.02 cm thick and possess energy upto 10 MeV.

Beta rays (β-rays). They consist of electrons (^0_1e) and are negatively charged. They are deflected by an electrostatic field and can penetrate an aluminium sheet upto 0.2 cm thick. The penetrating power of β-rays is more (about 10 times) as compared to that of α–rays.

Gamma rays (γ-rays). These are high energy electromagnetic radiations having a very short wave length (of the order of 10 pm) and are not deflected by electrostatic field as they do not carry any charge. They can penetrate through an aluminium sheet upto 100 cm thick.

Nucleides. The nuclei of atoms represented by their atomic numbers and mass numbers are called nucleides *e.g.* $^{235}_{92}U$ represents nucleide of uranium.

Nuclear Forces. The forces that hold the nuclear particles together are called nuclear forces. They are very strong forces, 30-40 times stronger than coulombic forces.

Nuclear Isomers. The atom having same atomic number and same mass number but with different radioactive properties are called

nuclear isomers *e.g.* $U\left(t_{\frac{1}{2}} = 1.4\right)$ and $U\left(t_{\frac{1}{2}} = 6.7\right)$.

Mass defect. It is the difference between the actual nuclear mass and expected nuclear mass (sum of the individual masses of nuclear particles).

Relationship between Mass Defect and Energy

$E = \Delta mc^2$, where, Δm is mass defect and c is the velocity of light.

Binding energy. It is the energy equivalent to mass defect and is responsible for holding the nucleus together. It is known as **binding energy of the nucleus.**

The parent element. The element which decays α-particles, β-rays, γ-rays etc., is known as parent element.

The daughter element. The element which is formed, when the parent element decays, α-, β- or γ- rays is known as daughter element.

α-decays. The radioactive decay in which an unstable nuclei ejects an α-particle is known as α-decay. The daughter element has a mass 4 units less than parent element and the atomic number of daughter element is 2 units less than that of the parent element

$$^{238}_{92}U \longrightarrow \quad ^{234}_{90}Th \quad + \quad ^{4}_{2}He$$
$$\text{(Parent)} \qquad \text{(Daughter)} \qquad \text{(α - particle)}$$

The daughter element will occupy a position which is two groups to the left of the parent element.

β-decay. The radioactive decay in which an unstable nuclei ejects an electron (b-particle). It arises from the conversion of a neutron in a nucleus into proton. Since mass numbers of a proton and a neutron are same, the emission of β-particle will not cause any change in the mass number of daughter element. However since the daughter element has one more proton as compared to the parent element so its atomic number increases by one unit and it occupies a position which is one group to the right of that of parent element.

$$^{14}_{6}C \longrightarrow {}^{14}_{7}N + {}^{0}_{-1}e$$
$$(\beta - \text{rays})$$

γ-decays. The emission of γ-rays do not bring about any changes either in mass number or in atomic number of the nucleus. Such an emission is observed in almost all nuclear reactions from nuclei which are left in an excited state by an earlier emission of an α- or β-particle.

Group displacement law. The *emission of α-rays* by an element results in the formation of new element which lies *two places left* to the parent element and the emission of a β-*particle* results in the formation of a new element which lies one *place right* to the parent element in the periodic table.

Radio-active disintegration series. The series of spontaneous changes that take place starting from the parent element (which has unstable nucleus) till the formation of an element with stable nucleus is called *radioactive disintegration series*.

Some of the important disintegration series are

(a) unranium series ($4n + 2$) series

(b) thorium series ($4n$) series

(c) actinium series ($4n + 3$) series

(d) neptunium series ($4n + 1$) series.

1.2 Atomic Orbitals

Quantum Mechanical Model of an Atom. The salient features of this model of atom are:

(i) Electron is a material wave *i.e.* it transfers its mass and charge as a unit, but its motion is a wave.

(ii) Particle waves do not belong to the spectrum of electromagnetic waves. They are never radiated by or lost from the particle, and their velocity is variable.

(iii) Electron wave is retained by the atomic nucleus.

(iv) The exact position and momentum of an electron cannot be calculated, but it is expressed as **probability** (mathematically, φ^2).

(v) The permitted energy of an electron is related by integers called **quantum numbers** (n, l, m, s).

Orbital wave function. The wave function for an electron in an atom or molecule is called an orbital wave function.

Orbital. The region in space around the nucleus where the probability of finding an electron is maximum, is called an orbital.

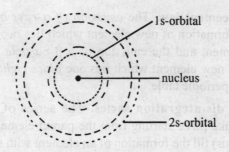

Fig. 1.1

Probability density. The square of wave function (φ^2) of an electron is called probability density of the electron.

The wave function depends upon two variables

(i) distance of the electron from the nucleus, and

(ii) two angles in three dimensional space.

Radial probability. The probability (φ^2) of finding an electron can be expressed as a function of distance 'r' from the nucleus. This is known as radial probability.

Angular probability. The probability (φ^2) of finding an electron can be expressed as a function of the angle it subtends with the nuclear axis. This is known as angular probability.

Radial probability distribution curves. A curve that shows the variation of wave function with distance from the nucleus is known as radial probability distribution curve.

The radial probability distribution curves for 1s and 2s orbitals are shown in diagram. (Fig. 1.2)

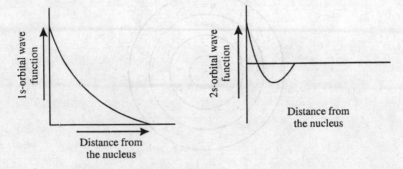

Fig. 1.2. Variation of wave function with distance.

Nodal surface. It is a surface on which the probability of finding a particular electron is zero.

Quantum numbers. In order to specify shape, size and energy of an electron orbital certain numbers are used. These numbers used to specify shape, size and energy of an electron orbital are called quantum numbers.

Quantum numbers may also be defined as a set of four integers which are necessary to locate the energy level or position of an electron and specify the shape, size and orientation of the orbital to which electron belongs.

Principal quantum number (n). It determines the distance of the electron from the nucleus. The orbit nearest to the nucleus is given the principal quantum number 1($n = 1$), the next 2 and so on. These *orbits* are also called *main energy levels* or *shells* and are also designated as K, L, M, N etc. for $n = 1, 2, 3, 4, ...$etc. respectively.

Angular momentum quantum number (l). It is also known as *azimuthal quantum number* or *orbital quantum number*. It determines the energy of the electrons due to angular momentum. The value of *l* indicates the *sub-levels* or *sub-shell* in which the electrons is located. The 'l' can have all possible values from 0 to $(n-1)$ for any shell. The various sub-shells are designated as s, p, d, f depending on the value of 'l'.

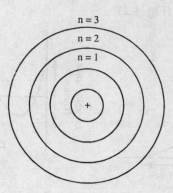

Fig. 1.3

It also determines the shape of the orbital

Value of l	Designation of sub-shell
0	s
1	p
2	d
3	f

Magnetic quantum number (m). It refers to different orientations of electron cloud in a particular sub-shell. These different orientations are called **orbitals.** The number of orbitals in a particular sub-shell with in a principal energy level is given by the values allowed to 'm' which in turn depends on values of 'l'. The possible values of 'm' range from $-l$ through 0 to $+l$, thus making a total of $(2l+1)$ values.

It determines the magnetic orientation of an orbital *i.e.* the direction of the orbital relative to magnetic field in which it is placed.

Spin quantum number (s). The spin quantum numbers(s) describes the rotation of electron about its own axis. It can have two values

+1/2 or –1/2. Thus for each value of '*m*' there are two possible values of *s*. The '*s*' values correspond to the orientation of magnetic field associated with the electron spin begin in the same or opposite to the applied magnetic field.

Schrodinger's Equation. The behaviour of an electron wave can be described by Schrodinger's wave equation

$$\frac{\partial^2 \varphi}{\partial x^2} + \frac{\partial^2 \varphi}{\partial y^2} + \frac{\partial^2 \varphi}{\partial z^2} + \frac{8\pi^2 m}{h^2}(E - V)\varphi = 0$$

where φ is called wave function, representing the amplitude of the wave

x, y, z are three coordinates in space

m is mass of electron, h is Plank's constant,

E and V are total energy and potential energy of the electron respectively.

Probability Density $(\psi)^2$

The orbital wave function, ψ, as such has no physical significance. It simply represents amplitude of the electron wave. However, square of wave function, ψ^2, is the measure of probability of finding the electron in a unit volume around a particular point and is called probability density. *A graph of ψ^2 as a function of distance from the nucleus* is called **probability density curve.** The probability density curves for 1*s* and 2*s* orbitals are shown in Fig. 1.4.

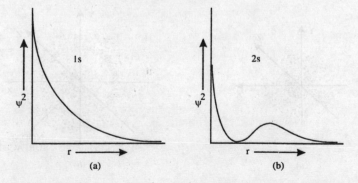

Fig. 1.4. (a) Probability density curve of 1*s* orbital. (b) Probability density curve of 2*s* orbital.

It may be noted that the probability of finding the electron does not become zero even at very large distances from the nucleus. Therefore, it is not possible to draw a boundary which will enclose regions of 100% probability. However, for the sake of clarity of representation we draw boundary surfaces which enclose regions of maximum probability (say 99%).

The regions of space around the nucleus where the probability of finding the electron is maximum are called orbitals.

The boundary surfaces of ψ^2 are quite similar to that of ψ. However, there is one main qualitative **difference** that ψ may have negative sign in some regions whereas ψ^2 is always positive.

Charge Clouds Pictures of Orbitals

An alternative way to describe the probability is in terms of negative charge cloud, the density of charge cloud being proportional to ψ^2 or probability. In this method, the charge cloud is represented in term of small dots. To understand, this method of representation let us imagine the electron as a very small dot. Let us further suppose that we take a very large number of photographs of the electron in a hydrogen atom at very short interval of time on the same film. If the film were developed, the picture obtained would be similar to that shown in Fig 1.5 (a). In terms of electron cloud representation the probability of finding the electron in a particular region of space is directly proportional to the density of such dots in that region.

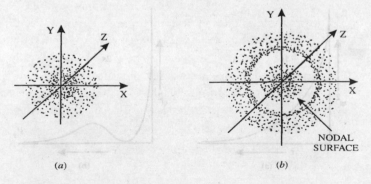

(a)   (b)

Fig. 1.5. (a) Charge cloud picture of $1s$ orbital. (b) Charge cloud picture of $2s$ orbital.

For **s-orbitals** the *probability of finding the electron is same in all directions* at a particular distance. The other words, **s-orbitals are spherically symmetrical.** The electron cloud picture of 1s orbital is shown in Fig. 1.10 (a). The *s*-orbitals of higher energy levels are also spherically symmetrical, however, they are more diffused and have spherical shells within them where probability of finding the electron is zero. These are called **spherical** or **radical nodes**. In 2*s* orbital [Fig 1.5 (b)] there is one spherical node. In the *ns* orbital, the number of such spherical nodes is $(n-1)$.

For **p-orbitals** there are three possible orientations of electron cloud. These three orientations or orbitals of a *p*-sub-shell are designated as p_x, p_y and p_z or p_{+1}, p_{-1} and p_0 respectively, p_x, p_y and p_z orbitals are oriented along *x*-axis, *y*-axis and *z*-axis respectively. Each *p*-orbital has two lobes which are separated by a plane of zero probability called **nodal plane.** Each *p* orbital is, thus, **dumb-bell shaped.** The spatial distributions of 2*p* orbitals are shown in Fig. 1.6.

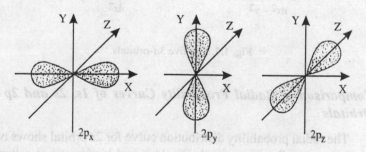

Fig. 1.6. 2*p* orbitals.

For **d-orbitals** there are five possible orientations of electron cloud. These five orientations or orbitals are designated as d_{xy}, d_{yz}, d_{xz}, $d_{x^2-y^2}$ and d_{z^2}. Three of these orbitals, d_{xy}, d_{yz} and d_{xz} are identical in shape but different in orientations. Each has four lobes of electron density bisecting the angles between principal axes.

The $d_{x^2-y^2}$ orbital also has four lobes which lie along *x* and *y* axes. The d_{z^2} orbital has two lobes lying along *z*-axis and a ring of hogh electron density in the *xy* plane as shown in Fig. 1.7.

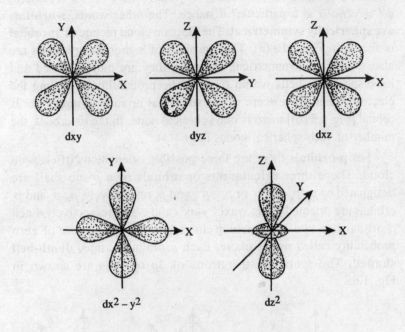

Fig. 1.7. The five 3*d*-orbitals.

Comparison of Radial Probability Curves of 1s, 2s and 2p Orbitals

The radial probability distribution curve for 2s orbital shows two maxima, a smaller one near the nucleus and bigger one at a larger distance. In between these two maxima, there is a maxima where there is no probability of finding the electron at that distance. The point at which the probability of finding the electron is zero is called a **nodal point.**

The distances of maximum probability for 2*s* and 2*p* orbitals are approximately the same but are larger than the distance of maximum probability for 1*s* orbital. This means that 2*s* and 2*p* electrons are at a greater distance than of 1*s* orbital. This is in keeping with the fact that 2*s* and 2*p* electrons have greater energy than that of the 1*s* electron.

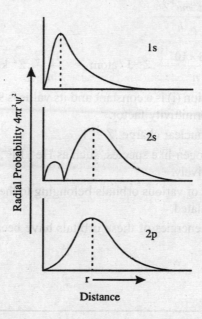

Fig. 1.8. Radial probability distribution curves for 1*s*, 2*s* and 2*p*-orbitals.

The radius of maximum probability for a 2*p* electron is slightly less than that for a 2*s* electron. However, in contrast to 2*p* curve, there is small additional maxima in the 2*s* curve. This indicates that the electron in 2*s* orbital spends some of its time near the nucleus. In other words, 2*s* electron penetrates a little closer to the nucleus, and is, therefore, held more tightly than the 2*p* electron.

Thus, 2*s* electron is more stable and has lower energy than a 2*p* electron.

Energy Level Diagram of Hydrogen Atom

In hydrogen atom there is only one electron which is present in 1*s* orbital in ground state. However, in excited state the electron may jump to any of the orbitals belonging to higher energy levels.

Energies of the higher energy levels for hydrogen atom and hydrogen-like species is given by the expression,

$$E_n = -k^2 \frac{2\pi^2 me^4 Z^2}{n^2 h^2} \qquad \qquad ...(i)$$

$$= -\frac{2.178 \times 10^{-18}}{n^2}.Z^2 \text{ J / atom} = -\frac{1312}{n^2}.Z^2 \text{ kJ / mole}$$

The k in relation (i) is a constant and its value is 9.0×10^9 J.m/C². k is inverse of permittivity factor.

For H atom nuclear charge, $Z = 1$

whereas for hydrogen-like species, such as He^+, Li^{2+}, Be^{+3}, Z is equal to 2, 3, 4 respectively.

The energies of various orbitals belonging to these energy levels can also be calculated.

The relative energies of these orbitals have been represented in Fig. 1.9. (a).

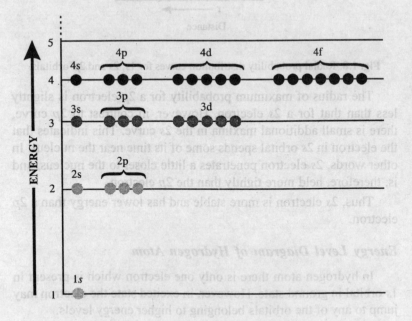

Fig. 1.9. (a) Energy level diagram of hydrogen atom.

It may be noted that all the orbitals of a particular energy level have same energy in hydrogen and hydrogen-like species. For example, 2s and 2p orbitals have same energy. *It is so because for an atom having a single electron, the principal quantum number, n is most important in determining the energy of the orbital. The value of l (the angular momentum quantum number) merely determines the shape of the orbital.*

Hydrogenic Ions: These are the ions having one electron *e.g.* He⁺, Li²⁺ etc. Schrodinger's equation can be applied to these ions.

The average radius *r* of an orbital is

$$r = n^2 \cdot \frac{a_0}{z}$$

where a_0 = Bohri radius (59 pm), the average radius of 1s orbital in hydrogen.

$$En = -\frac{Z^2 R}{n^2}$$

The factor z^2 arises because the electron-nuclear interaction at a given distance has increased by Z, and the average distance has also decreased by Z. Thus ionization energy of He⁺ ($z = 2$) is four times that of H and that of Li²⁺ ($z = 3$) is nine times that of H.

1.3 Many Electron Atoms

Energy Level Diagram of Multi-electron Atoms

In case of multi-electron atoms the energies of various orbitals depend not only upon the nuclear charge but also upon the other electrons present in the atom. It is impossible to calculate the exact energies of various orbitals in a multi-electron atom. However, approximate values of their energies can be obtained from the special data. Relative order of energies of various orbitals in all multi-electron atoms is same and is illustrated in Fig. 1.10.

When the electrons occupy the orbitals of lowest energy, it is called **ground state** of the atom.

The energy required to excite or remove one electron is conveniently represented by **orbital energy** (E). Thus,

Ionization Energy (I) = $-E_1$

It is commonly known as **Koopman's theorem**. It is also called Koopman's approximation.

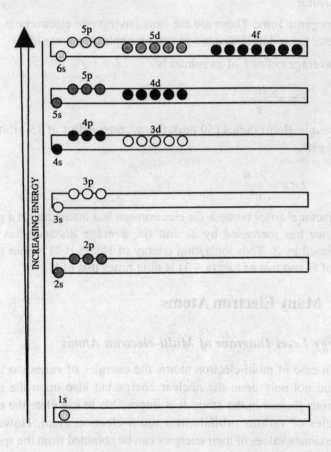

Fig. 1.10. Energy level diagram of multi-electron atoms.

Electron Spin. It is one of the quantum numbers (*i.e.*, spin quantum number). It can have two values +1/2 and –1/2. Generally these two states are called **spin up** and **spin down** or denoted by Greek letters α and β.

If two electrons in an orbital have same spin they are called **spin paired (parallel spin)**. The atoms having unpaired electrons are **paramagnetic** in nature (*i.e.* they attract magnetic substances) and atoms with zero unpaired electrons are **diamagnetic** (they are repelled by magnetic field).

Spectroscopy. It deals with the study of the radiation emitted or absorbed. This technique is quite useful in the study of arrangement of electrons in an atom.

Electromagnetic spectrum. The arrangement of various electromagnetic radiations in order of decreasing frequencies or increasing wavelengths is known as electromagnetic spectrum.

Different regions of the spectrum are known by different names as shown in Fig. 1.11.

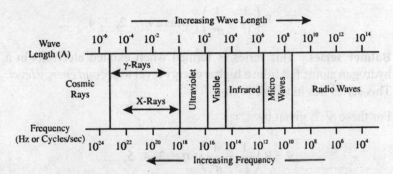

Fig. 1.11. Electromagnetic spectrum.

Various types of electromagnetic radiations. The various types of electromagnetic radiations are radiowaves, micro-waves, infra-red waves, ultraviolet waves, visible light, X-rays, γ-rays, cosmic rays etc.

Atomic Spectra. The emission spectrum of elements consists of discrete sharp lines having different wavelength separated by dark bands is called *atomic spectrum*. It is characteristic of an element. Each element has a characteristic pattern of lines.

Spectroscope. It is an instrument that is used for observing spectrum by use of a prism or a grating. A spectroscope is also known as a **spectrometer.**

Hydrogen spectrum. When an electric discharge is passed through hydrogen gas at low pressure, some hydrogen atoms are formed which emit light in visible region. It has been found to comprise of series of lines of different wavelengths. Some of the important series of hydrogen spectrum are

(i) Lyman series (ii) Balmer series (iii) Paschen series (iv) Brackett series (v) Pfund series.

Lyman series. This series is formed when excited electrons in a hydrogen atoms fall from a higher energy level to *first level*. This series of lines is observed in *ultraviolet region*.

For these $\bar{v}$ (wave number) is given by

$$\bar{v} = R\left(\frac{1}{1^2} - \frac{1}{n^2}\right), \text{ where } n = 2, 3, 4, \ldots\ldots$$

Balmer series. This series is formed when excited electrons in a hydrogen atoms fall from a higher energy level to *second energy level*. This series lies in *visible region*.

For these $\bar{v}$ is given by

$$\bar{v} = R\left(\frac{1}{2^2} - \frac{1}{n^2}\right); n = 3, 4, 5, \ldots\ldots$$

Paschen series. This series is formed when electrons in hydrogen atoms fall from a higher energy level to *third energy level*. This series lies in *infra-red region*.

$$\bar{v} = R\left(\frac{1}{3^2} - \frac{1}{n^2}\right); n = 4, 5, 6, \ldots\ldots$$

Brackett series. This series is formed when excited electrons in hydrogen atoms fall from higher energy levels to *fourth energy level*. It lies in *infra-red region*.

$$\bar{v} = R\left(\frac{1}{4^2} - \frac{1}{n^2}\right); \; n = 5, 6, 7, \ldots\ldots$$

Pfund series. This series formed when excited electrons in hydrogen atom fall from higher energy levels to *fifth energy level*. It lies in *infra-red region*.

$$\bar{v} = R\left(\frac{1}{5^2} - \frac{1}{n^2}\right); \; n = 6, 7, 8, \ldots\ldots$$

Zeeman effect. The splitting of spectral lines in a strong magnetic field is called *Zeeman* effect. It is associated with magnetic quantum number.

Stark effect. The splitting of electric lines in electric field is known as *stark effect*.

Pauli's Exclusion Principle. It states, "No two electrons in an atom can have the same values for all the four quantum numbers."

Effective Nuclear charge. The electrostatic force of repulsion between negatively charged electrons influences the energies of the orbitals. The effect of repulsion is called **screening effect** or **stulding effect**. The combined effect of attraction of the nucleus and repulsion from other electrons gives an **effective nuclear charge** (Z_{eff}), which is less than Z of the 'bare' nucleus

$$E = -\frac{Z^2_{eff} \cdot R}{n^2}$$

where R = Rydberg constant

n = principal quantum number.

The difference between 'bare' and effective nuclear charge is **screening constant**, σ.

$$\sigma = Z - Z_{eff}$$

For $1 + e$ the value of σ is 0.66, it shows that the effects of repulsion from one electron an another has an effect equivalent to reducing the nuclear charge by 0.66 units.

Screening and Penetration

If we look at the energy level diagrams for hydrogen atom (Fig. 1.9) and that of multielectron atoms (Fig. 1.10) we find that in case of hydrogen the orbitals $2s$ and $2p$ are **degenerate** (*i.e.* have same energy) and in case of multielectron atoms the energy of $2s$ is lower as compared to that of $2p$. This is due to screening effect or penetration effect.

Hunds' Rule. It states, "when electrons are placed in a set of degenerate orbitals, the ground state has as many electrons as possible in different orbitals and with parallel spin.

Extra-stability of Half-filled and completely filled orbitals. Half-filled or completely filled orbitals have extra-stability because they are more symmetrical and have lower energy because of least repulsion than the incompletely filled orbitals.

Iso-electronic ions. Ions which have the same number of electrons are called isoelectronic ions, *i.e.* O^{2-}, Na^+, Al^{3+} and Ne all have 10 electrons so they are isoelectronic.

Nodal plane. It is the plane around the nucleus where the probability of finding the electron is zero.

In case of p-orbitals the nodal plane passes through the centre of the nucleus.

1.4   The Periodic Table

It is a table in which the elements are arranged horizontally in **periods** and vertically in **groups** according to their chemical similarity.

In the modern periodic table the elements have been arranged in the order of their increasing atomic numbers.

Atomic numbers were determined by x-ray spectra in 1917 **(Mooseley's studies).** Mooseley observed that in each series the frequency (ν) of each line matched with atomic number (z) according to the formula

$$\nu = c\,(z - \sigma)^2$$

where c and σ are constants for a given series.

Auf-bau Principle. According to it the ground state electron configuration of an atom can be found by putting electrons in orbitals starting with lowest energy and moving progressively to higher energy.

Following this the structures of atoms are shown below.

The Electron Configuration of the Element

Atomic Number	Symbol	Electron Configuration	Atomic Number	Symbol	Electron Configuration
1.	H	$1s^1$	2.	He	$1s^2$
3.	Li	$[He]2s^1$	4.	Be	$[He]2s^2$
5.	B	$[He]2s^22p^1$	6.	C	$[Hc]2s^22p^2$
7.	N	$[He]2s^22p^3$	8.	O	$[He]2s^22p^4$
9.	F	$[He]2s^22p^5$	10.	Ne	$[He]2s^22p^6$
11.	Na	$[Ne]3s^1$	12.	Mg	$[Ne]3s^2$
13.	Al	$[Ne]3s^23p^1$	14.	Si	$[Ne]3s^23p^2$
15.	P	$[Ne]3s^23p^3$	16.	S	$[Ne]3s^23p^4$
17.	Cl	$[Ne]3s^23p^5$	18.	Ar	$[Ne]3s^23p^6$
19.	K	$[Ar]4s^1$	20.	Ca	$[Ar]4s^2$
21.	Sc	$[Ar]4s^23d^1$	22.	Ti	$[Ar]4s^23d^2$
23.	V	$[Ar]4s^23d^3$	*24.	Cr	$[Ar]4s^13d^5$
25.	Mn	$[Ar]4s^23d^5$	26.	Fe	$[Ar]4s^23d^6$
27.	Co	$[Ar]4s^23d^7$	28.	Ni	$[Ar]4s^23d^8$
*29.	Cu	$[Ar]4s^13d^{10}$	30.	Zn	$[Ar]4s^23d^{10}$
31.	Ga	$[Ar]4s^23d^{10}4p^1$	32.	Ge	$[Ar]4s^23d^{10}4p^2$
33.	As	$[Ar]4s^23d^{10}4p^3$	34.	Sc	$[Ar]4s^23d^{10}4p^4$
35.	Br	$[Ar]4s^23d^{10}4p^5$	36.	Kr	$[Ar]4s^23d^{10}4p^6$
37.	Rb	$[Kr]5s^1$	38.	Sr	$[Kr]5s^2$
39.	Y	$[Kr]5s^24d^1$	40.	Zr	$[Kr]5s^24d^2$
*41.	Nb	$[Kr]5s^14d^4$	*42.	Mo	$[Kr]5s^14d^5$
43.	Tc	$[Kr]5s^24d^5$	*44.	Ru	$[Kr]5s^14d^7$
*45.	Rh	$[Kr]5s^14d^8$	*46.	Pb	$[Kr]4d^{10}$
*47.	Ag	$[Kr]5s^14d^{10}$	48.	Cd	$[Kr]5s^24d^{10}$
49.	In	$Kr]5s^24d^{10}5p^1$	50.	Sn	$[Kr]5s^24d^{10}5p^2$

(Contd.)

Atomic Number	Symbol	Electron Configuration	Atomic Number	Symbol	Electron Configuration
51.	Sb	$[Kr]5s^24d^{10}5p^3$	52.	Te	$[Kr]5s^24d^{10}5p^4$
53.	I	$[Kr]5s^24d^{10}5p^5$	54.	Xe	$[Kr]5s^24d^{10}5p^6$
55.	Cs	$[Xe]6s^1$	56.	Ba	$[Xe]6s^2$
*57.	La	$[Xe]6s^25d^1$	*58.	Ce	$[Xe]6s^24f^15d^1$
59.	Pr	$[Xe]6s^24f^3$	60.	Nd	$[Xe]6s^24f^4$
61.	Pm	$[Xe]6s^24f^5$	62.	Sm	$[Xe]6s^24f^6$
63.	Eu	$[Xe]6s^24f^7$	*64.	Gd	$[Xe]6s^24f^75d^1$
65.	Tb	$[Xe]6s^24f^9$	66.	Dy	$[Xe]6s^24f^{10}$
67.	Ho	$[Xe]6s^24f^{11}$	68.	Er	$[Xe]6s^24f^{12}$
69.	Tm	$[Xe]6s^24f^{13}$	70.	Yb	$[Xe]6s^24f^{14}$
71.	Lu	$[Xe]6s^24f^{14}5d^1$	72.	Hf	$[Xe]6s^24f^{14}5d^2$
73.	Ta	$[Xe]6s^24f^{14}5d^3$	74.	W	$[Xe]6s^24f^{14}5d^4$
75.	Re	$[Xe]6s^24f^{14}5d^5$	76.	Os	$[Xe]6s^24f^{14}5d^6$
77.	Ir	$[Xe]6s^24f^{14}5d^7$	*78.	Pt	$[Xe]6s^24f^{14}5d^9$
*79.	Au	$[Xe]6s^14f^{14}5d^{10}$	80.	Hg	$[Xe]6s^24f^{14}5d^{10}$
81.	Tl	$[Xe]6s^24f^{14}5d^{10}6p^1$	82.	Pb	$[Xe]6s^24f^{14}5d^{10}6p^2$
83.	Bi	$[Xe]6s^24f^{14}5d^{10}6p^3$	84.	Po	$[Xe]6s^24f^{14}5d^{10}6p^4$
85.	At	$[Xe]6s^24f^{14}5d^{10}6p^5$	86.	Rn	$[Xe]6s^24f^{14}5d^{10}6p^6$
87.	Fr	$[Rn]7s^1$	88.	Ra	$[Rn]7s^2$
89.	Ac	$[Rn]7s^26d^1$	90.	Th	$[Rn]7s^26d^2$
91.	Pa	$[Rn]7s^25f^26d^1$	92.	U	$[Rn]7s^25f^36d^1$
93.	Np	$[Rn]7s^25f^46d^1$	94.	Pu	$[Rn]7s^25f^6$
95.	Am	$[Rn]7s^25f^7$	*96.	Cm	$[Rn]7s^25f^76d^1$
97.	Bk	$[Rn]7s^25f^9$	98.	Cf	$[Rn]7s^25f^{10}$
99.	Es	$[Rn]7s^25f^{11}$	100.	Fm	$[Rn]7s^25f^{12}$
101.	Md	$[Rn]7s^25f^{13}$	102.	No	$[Rn]7s^25f^{14}$
103.	Lr	$[Rn]7s^25f^{14}6d^1$	104.	Unq[104]	$[Rn]7s^25f^{14}6d^2$
105.	Unp[105]	$[Rn]7s^25f^{14}6d^3$	106.	Unh[106]	$[Rn]7s^25f^{15}6d^4$
107.	Uns[107]	$[Rn]7s^25f^{14}6d^5$	108.	Uno[108]	$[Rn]7s^25f^{14}6d^6$
109.	Une[109]	$[Rn]7s^25f^{14}6d^7$	110.	[110]	$[Rn]7s^25f^{14}6d^8$
111.	[111]	$[Rn]7s^25f^{14}6d^9$	112.	[112]	$[Rn]7s^25f^{14}6d^{10}$

*Elements have exceptional elelctronic Configuration

The **inner shell** orbitals denoted by square brackets are too tightly bound to be involved in chemical reactions. The **valence** and **outer electron** determine chemical properties.

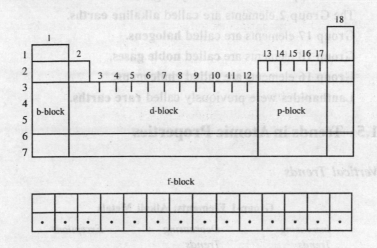

Fig. 1.12

Block Structure. In the **Long form** of periodic table there are **four blocks** in which all the elements have been group. The elements in any block have similar properties. The four blocks are called *s-block*, *p-block*, *d-block* and *f-block*.

The *s-block* has two groups (Group 1 and 2)

The *p-block* has six groups (Group 13, 14, 15, 16, 17, 18)

The *d-block* has ten groups (Groups 3, 4, 5, 6, 7, 8, 9, 10, 11, 12)

The *f-block* is placed at the bottom of the table and has 14 elements each in two rows.

The *s*- and *p*- blocks are collectively called **main groups**. The elements in them are called **main group elements** or **representative elements**.

The *d-block* elements are called **Transition elements.**

The *f-block* elements are called **inner-transition elements.**

The *f-block* elements include **lanthanides and actinides.**

Group Numbers and Names

Groups are numbered from 1 to 18.

The **Group 1** elements (not hydrogen) are called **alkali metals.**

The **Group 2** elements are called **alkaline earths.**

Group 17 elements are called **halogens.**

Group 18 elements are called **noble gases.**

Group 16 elements are called **chalcogens.**

Lanthanides were previously called **rare earths.**

1.5 Trends in Atomic Properties

Vertical Trends

Group-1 Elements; Alkali Metals

	Increasing Trends	Decreasing Trends	Exceptions
Li	Atomic Radii (M)	Ionisation Energy	
	Ionic Radii M^+ (g)	Ionic size M^+ (aq)	Density of K < Na
Na	Density	Extent of Hydration of M^+	
	Electropositive character	$\Delta H_{Hydration}$ of M^+	Li has lowest $E°$ value
K	Chemical reactivity	Stability of hydrides (MH)	Li is strongest reducing agent
Rb	$E°$ values	Strength of intermetallic bonds	
Cs	Basic strength of metal hydroxides (MOH)	Melting and boiling points	
		Wavelength of colour imparted to flame	
*Fr	Tendency to form peroxides and super oxides		
ns^1	Reducing nature of metal hydroxides (MH)		

Group-2 Elements; Alkaline Earth Metals

	Increasing Trends	Decreasing Trends	Exceptions
Be	Atomic Radii (M)	IE_1 and IE_2 values	Density of Ca < Mg
	Ionic radii (M^{2+})	Electronegativity	Halides of Be are covalent

Mg	Density	Tendency to form comple-	BeO and Be $(OH)_2$ are
Ca	Reducing nature (E° values)	xes diminishes after Mg	amphoteric
	Reactivity	Solubility of CO_3^{2-} and SO_4^{2-}	
Sr	Tendency to form peroxides		
Ba	Basic strength of hydroxides		
	Solubility of hydroxides in water		
Ra	Ionic nature of halides		
ns^2			

Group-13 Elements

	Increasing Trends	*Decreasing Trends*	*Exceptions*
B	Atomic Radii(M)	Ionisation energies	Atomic size if Ga < In
	Ionic Radii		IE_1 of Tl > In
Al	Inert pair effect		IE_1 of Ga $\approx$ Al
	Tendency to show + 1 oxidation state	M.P./B.P.	
Ga	Tendency to form ionic compounds	Tendency to show + 3 oxidation state	
In	Electropositive character	Tendency to form covalent	
Tl	Lewis acid strength of trihalides of B increases from $BF_3 \rightarrow BBr_3$	compounds	
ns^2			
np^1			

Behaviour of $M(OH)_3$ change from **acidic** $\rightarrow$ **amphoteric** $\rightarrow$ **basic**

Compunds of Boron and hydrogen are BORANES which contains three centre 2 electron bond

Compunds of aluminium are ionic as well as covalent.

Group-14 Elements

	Increasing Trends	*Decreasing Trends*	*Exceptions*
C	Atomic Radii	Ionisation energy	IE of Pb > Sn
	Inner part effect	Electronegativity	IE of Ge $\approx$ Si
Si	Metallic character	Non-metallic character	Only C has ability of
Ge	Tendency of + 2 oxidation state	Tendency of + 4 oxidation state	$p\pi$-$p\pi$ bonding

(Contd.)

Sn	Tendency of forming ionic compounds	Tendency of forming compounds	Si and others can form $d\pi$-$p\pi$ bonding
Pb	Reducing character of hydrides (MH_4)	Thermal stability of hydrides	All elements except Pb show allotropy
ns^2		M—M bond strength	
np^2		Tendency of catenation	

They form oxides of formula MO and MO_2

Behaviour of MO_2 change from acidic → amphoteric → weakly basic

Group-15 Elements

	Increasing Trends	Decreasing Trends	Exceptions
N	Atomic Size	Ionisation energies	N, O show oxidation state
	Melting/Boiling points increase from N → As	Electronegativity M.P./B.P. decrease As → Bi	–3 to +5 Bi show oxidation state of +3 only
P	Metal Character	Tendency of covalent bonding	Elements excepts N, Bi exhibit alotropy
As	Density	Thermal stability of hydrides	B.P. of MH_3 $Ph_3 < AsH_3 < NH_3 < SbH_3$
	Tendency of lower oxidation state +3	Angle around M in metal hydrides (MH_3)	$< BiH_3$
Sb	Reducing character of hydrides (MH_3)	Basic nature of MH_3 Acidic character of oxides	
Bi	Ionic character of comp. dominate toward end	Tendency of forming MX_5	
ns^2			
np^3			

Behaviour of oxides change from acidic → amphoteric → basic →

Their hydrides MH_3 and trihalides are pyramidal but pentahalides are trigonal bipyramidal

Group-16 Elements; Chalcogens

	Increasing Trends	Decreasing Trends	Exceptions
	Atomic size	Ionisation energies	O shows tendency of $p\pi$-$p\pi$ bonding other can form
O	Density Ionic radius	Electronegativity M.P./B.P. decrease, Te → Po	dp-pp bonding EA_1 of O $<$ $EA_1$of S
S	M.P./B.P. increase, O → Te	Electron affinity Thermal stability of H_2X	S shows some tendency of catenation

	Metallic character	Bond angle around X	X—X bond strength is
Se	Acidic nature if hydrides	X—X bond strength	highest
Te	(H_2X)		
*Po			
ns^2	B.P. of H_2X : $H_2O > H_2Se > H_2Te > H_2S$		
np^4	Atomicity of O is 2 in O_2, 3 in O_3, but those of S, Se, Te is 8		
	O shows O.N. of $-2, -1, +1, +2$; S shows $-2, +2, +4, +6$; other show $+2, +4$		

Group-17 Elements; Halogens

	Increasing Trends	*Decreasing Trends*	*Exceptions*
	Atomic size	Ionisation energy	
F	Ionic radii X^-	Electronegativity	
	Melting/Boiling points	Electron affinity	EA_1 of Cl > EA_1 of F
Cl	Intensity of colour	Chemical reactivity	
	Electropositive character	E° values	
Br	Acidic nature of hydrides (HX)	Oxidising power	
I	Reducing nature of hydrides (HX)	Thermal stability of HX $\Delta H_{diss.}$ of H—X	
*At		Acid strength of HOX	
ns^2	Molecular state X_2		
np^5	Dissociation energy $[X_2(g) \to 2X(g)]I_2 < F_2 < Br_2 < Cl_2$		
	F shows oxidation state of -1 ; others show oxidation state $-1, +1, +3, +5, +7$		
	Strength of oxoacids increase in oxidation number of X.		

Group-18 Elements; Noble Gases

	Increasing Trends	*Decreasing Trends*	*Exceptions*
He	Atomic size		
	Polarisability	Ionisation energy	
Ne	Magnitude of van der Waal forces M.P./B.P.		
Ar	Ease of liquefaction		
Kr	Solubility in water		
Xe	Reactivity		
*Rn			
ns^2	Molecular state is monoatomic		
np^6	Xe shows oxidation state of $+2, +4, +6$		

Horizontal Trends

Increasing Z_{eff} leads to an **increase** in **ionization energy (IE)** across each period. Similar trends are observed in **electron affinity (EA)**. These are shown in Fig. 1.13.

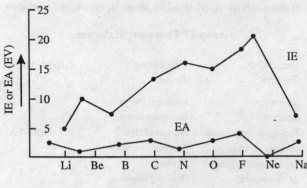

Fig. 1.13

These trends are sometimes cited as evidence for special stability of filled and half-filled shells.

States of Ionisation. The values of successive I.E.–increase with the degree of ionization *i.e.*

$$IE_1 < IE_2 < IE_3 \ldots$$

The value of **electron affinity** (EA) is always less than that of ionization energy because of extra electron repulsion involved.

Some atoms have negative electron affinities. Meaning that negative ion is not stable in gas phase.

Second and subsequent electron affinities are always negative because of high degree of repulsion involved in formed a multiple charged negative ion.

Relative Effects

The two important effects of charged particles are **magnetic effects** and **electric effects.**

The **special theory of relativity** predicts effects such as enhancement of mass of fast moving particles.

The effects were included in **Dirac equation.**

The energies of orbitals also get altered, especially for electrons close to highly charged nuclei. Inner shells are most affected but they are not of much importance in chemistry.

Relativistic effects increase the **building energies** of the electrons and so they contribute to the irregularities in group trends and make appreciable contribution to high I.E. and hence chemical inertness of some heavy element (*e.g.* Gold and mercury).

Introduction to Inorganic Substances

2.1 Electronegativity and Bond Type

Electronegativity. It is the power of an atom to attract electrons to itself in a chemical bond.

It is an important parameter to determine the type of bonds formed between atoms.

Many a scales have been devised for electronegativity. Important of these are

(i) **Pauling Scale of Electronegativity.** It is based on bond energy and was the first to be devised. It lacks theoretical justification.

(ii) **Mulliken Electronegativity.** It takes into account both ionization energy and electron affinity values of an atom. The values on this scale can be estimated not only for the ground state, but for other electron configurations and even for polyatomic fragments.

(iii) **Allred-Rochow Electronegativity.** It is proportional to, $\dfrac{Z_{eff}}{r^2}$

where Z_{eff} is the **effective nuclear charge** of valence orbitals, and r is the **covalent radius** of the atom.

Each scale produces different numbers and they should not be mixed.

Generally electronegativity increases towards the right and decreases down the bottom in the periodic table.

The elements with low values of electronegativity (Group 1 and Group 2) are called **electropositive.**

The Bonding Triangle. It is a useful way to represent how the electronegativities of two elements A and B (which may be the same) determine the type of bond formed between them. The horizontal and vertical scales show the Pauling electronegativity values of the two elements. Pure elements (A = B) appear on the diagonals and various compounds are shown within the triangle (Fig. 2.1).

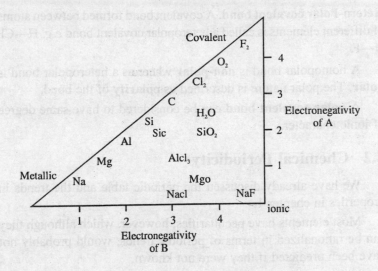

Fig. 2.1. The Bonding Triangle.

In this diagram the three basic regions are: —

1. When **both** A and B are **electropositive**, they form a **metallic bond.** Such a bond involves **delocalization of electrons** and the electrons are shared between atoms but in less specific way and without directional character.

2. When **both** A ands B are **electronegative**, they form **covalent bond** (e.g. O_2, H_2O etc.). Such a bond involves the **sharing of electrons** in specific, **localized bonds** between atoms.

The compounds/solids formed in this fashion may consist of **individual molecules** or **giant polymeric solids** with continuous network of bonds.

3. When one atom is very **electropositive** and the other is very **electronegative** an **ionic bond** is formed.

Bond Polarity

Homopolar covalent bond. A covalent bond between two atoms of the same element is called a homopolar covalent bond e.g. H—H, F—F, Cl—Cl etc.

Hetero-Polar covalent bond. A covalent bond formed between atoms of different elements is called a heteropolar covalent bond *e.g.* H—Cl, H—F.

A homopolar bond is **non-polar** where as a heteropolar bond is **polar**. The polar nature is described as **polarity** of the bond.

A **polar covalent bond** can be considered to have same degree of ionic character.

2.2 Chemical Periodicity

We have already discussed the periodic table and the trends in properties in chapter 1.

Most elements have peculiarities, however, which although they can be rationalized in terms of periodic trends, would probably not have been predicted if they were not known.

Metallic and Non-metallic Elements

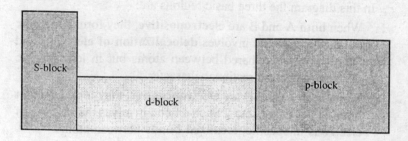

All the elements can be classified as **metals** and **non-metals**.

Metals are solids, good conductors, have a lustre, are malleable and ductile etc.

Non-metals have no lustre, are bad conductors, are neither malleable non-ductile (they are brittle) etc.

All the elements of s-, d- and f- blocks are metallic (except hydrogen).

Non-metals are found in upper right hand portion of p-block

Metals are

(i)   Good reducing agents

(ii) Form hydrated catious

(iii) Form solid halides and oxides

(iv) Their hydrides are solids with some ionic (H⁻) character

Non-metals

(i)   Form ionic compounds with electropositive metals

(ii) Form anions in water or oxoanions

(iii) Form molecular hydrides and halides

Metalloids: Non-metallic elements close to metallic borderline (Si, Ge, As, Sb, Se, Te) show less tendency to anionic behaviour are called **metalloids.**

The horizontal and vertical trends have already been discussed in chapter 1.

Main group (s-block and p-block) elements generally form ions with **closed shell** configurations (e.g. Na^+, Mg^{2+}, Al^{3+}) in which all electrons have been lost from the valence shell, an anions (F^-, O^{2-}) in which valence shell has been filled.

On moving down a group there is an increase in coordination number because of increase in size e.g. BeF_2 (CN = 4), MgF_2 (CN = 6) $Ca F_2$ (CN = 8).

For each block (s-, p-, A-), the first series involved has somewhat distinct chemistry compared with subsequent ones. Hydrogen is different from other s-block elements, the 2p-series (B–F) is different from others, 3d-series is different from 4d and 5d-series etc.

2.3　Stability and Reactivity

Stability and reactivity can be controlled by thermodynamic factors or kinetic factors. Both of these depend on the conditions and on the possibility of different routes to decomposition or reaction.

Some substances are thermodynamically stable whereas some may be kinetically stable e.g. B_2H_6, Si H_4 are thermodynamically unstable with respect to their elements but in the absence of heat or catalyst they became quite stable.

The unknown Ca F(s) is probably thermodynamically stable with respect to the elements themselves, but certainly unstable (thermodynamically and kinetically) with respect to the reaction

$$2Ca\ F\ (s) \rightarrow Ca\ (s) + Ca\ F_2\ (s)$$

Thermodynamic and kinetic factors are temperature dependent and they also depend on other conditions e.g. Ca F(g) can be formed as gas phase molecule at high temperature and low pressure.

Enthalpy and Hess's Law

Enthalpy (H) is the total **heat content** of the **system.**

Change in Enthalpy (ΔH) is a reaction is equal to the heat input under conditions of constant temperature and pressure.

For **endothermic reaction,** ΔH is **positive** and for **exothermic reaction,** ΔH is **negative**.

Hess's Law. It states, that ΔH is independs of path adopted to accomplish a change. It remains unchanged whether the change is carried out in our step or in a number of steps

i.e.　　　$\Delta H = \Delta H_1 + \Delta H_2 + \cdots\cdots\cdots\cdots\cdots$

Since **Enthalpy change** (ΔH) depends on conditions of temperature, pressure, concentration of initial and final states, it is important to specify these.

The **Standard state** of a substance is its state under standard pressure (one atmosphere) and 298 K.

The **standard enthalpy of formation** (ΔH_F°) of any substance is its enthalpy of formation from its elements in their standard state.

Various Types of Enthalpies

Change in enthalpy (ΔH). The heat energy that is exchanged between the system and the surroundings in a chemical reaction which is carried out at constant pressure is known as change in enthalpy (ΔH)

$$\Delta H = \Delta E + P\Delta V$$

Also $\qquad \Delta H = \Delta E + \Delta nRT \qquad [P\Delta V = \Delta nRT]$

Where $\Delta n =$ (number of moles of gaseous products–number of moles of gaseous reactants.)

Thermodynamic process. It refers to a series of intermediate steps that occur when a system changes from well defined initial state to a well defined final state.

It may also be defined as the path of change of a system from one equilibrium state to another.

Heat of reaction (Enthalpy of reaction). It is the enthalpy (or heat) change accompanying the conversion of as many moles of reactants to products as indicated by the given chemical reaction *e.g.*,

$$C(s) + H_2O(g) \rightarrow CO(g) + H_2(g); \qquad \Delta H = + 131.3 \text{ kJ.}$$

Enthalpy of a reaction depends upon the following factors:

(i) *Physical state* of reactants and products *e.g.*,

$$H_2(g) + \tfrac{1}{2} O_2(g) \rightarrow H_2O(g); \qquad \Delta H = -241.8 \text{ kJ.}$$
$$H_2(g) + \tfrac{1}{2} O_2(g) \rightarrow H_2O(l); \qquad \Delta H = -285.7 \text{ kJ.}$$

(ii) *Conditions of reaction.* When the reaction is carried out at constant volume $\Delta H = \Delta E$ and when it occurs at constant pressure, then

$$\Delta H = \Delta E + P\Delta V$$

(iii) *Temperature.* ΔH also depend upon the temperature of reaction. Kirchoff's equations are

$$\frac{\Delta H_2 - \Delta H_1}{T_2 - T_1} = \Delta C_p; \frac{\Delta E_2 - \Delta E_1}{T_2 - T_1} = \Delta C_v.$$

Enthalpy of formation. The enthalpy of formation of a compound at the given temperature may be defined as the enthalpy change when one mole of a compound in its standard state is formed form its elements (in their standard state). It is usually denoted by $D\overset{\circ}{H}_f$ e.g.,

$$C(\text{graphite}) + O_2(g) \rightarrow CO_2(g) ; \qquad \Delta H_f = -393.0 \text{ kJ.}$$
$$C(\text{graphite}) + 2H_2(g) \rightarrow CH_4(g) ; \qquad \Delta H_f = -74.8 \text{ kJ.}$$

Standard enthalpy of formation. The enthalpy of formation of a substance at 25°C (298 K) temperature and 1 atmosphere pressure is known as standard enthalpy of formation. It is denoted by $\Delta H°_f$.

> The standard enthalpies of formation for all elements in uncombined state are arbitrarily taken as zero.

> The enthalpy of formation of a compound is the enthalpy of the reaction in which it is formed from the elements in their native state.

> More the enthalpy of formation less will be the stability of a compound.

> A negative value of enthalpy of formation of a compound indicates that the compound is quite stable.

Enthalpy of combustion. It is the enthalpy change accompanying the complete combustion of one mole of the substance in excess of oxygen or air at that temperature e.g.,

$$H_2(g) + \tfrac{1}{2} O_2(g) \longrightarrow H_2O(l); \qquad \Delta H = -286 \text{ kJ.}$$

Enthalpy of combustion is always negative.

Enthalpy of fusion. It is the change in enthalpy when one mole of a solid changes into liquid completely at its melting point e.g.,

$$H_2O(s) \longrightarrow H_2O(l); \qquad \Delta H = 6 \text{ kJ.}$$

Enthalpy of vapourisation. It is the enthalpy change that accompanies the change of 1 mole of a liquid into vapour state completely at its boiling point e.g.,

$$H_2O(l) \longrightarrow H_2O(g); \qquad \Delta H = 30.56 \text{ kJ.}$$

Enthalpy of sublimation. It is the enthalpy change that occurs when 1 mole of a sublime solid changes into its vapours.

Enthalpy of solution. It is defined as the enthalpy change when one mole of the solute is dissolved in excess of solvent.

Enthalpy of neutralisation. It is defined as the enthalpy change accompanying the neutralisation of one gram equivalent of a base by an acid in dilute solution at that temperature, *e.g.*,

$$NaOH(aq) + HCl(aq) \longrightarrow NaCl(aq) + H_2O(l); \quad \Delta H = -57.1 \text{ kJ.}$$

- In case of strong base and a strong acid the value of enthalpy of neutralisation is same (*i.e.*, -57.1 kJ/mole).
- In case of a weak acid or a weak base its value is less than the above value.

Heat of ionization. It is the heat absorbed when 1 mole of an electrolyte completely dissociated into ions *e.g.*,

$$H_2SO_4 \rightleftharpoons 2H^+ + SO_4^{2-}; \qquad \Delta H = \text{(positive)}$$

Heat of hydration. It is the heat change that occurs when 1 mole of anhydrous salt combines with the required number of water molecules to form hydrated salt *e.g.*,

$$CuSO_4(s) + 5H_2O \longrightarrow CuSO_4 \cdot 5H_2O(s); \quad DH = -18.8 \text{ kcal.}$$

Lavosier and Laplace law. It states, "the amount of heat evolved or absorbed in chemical change is equal to heat evolved or absorbed when the reaction is reversed".

Hess's law. It states, "the enthalpy change of a chemical reaction remains the same whatever be the intermediate steps".

This law can be used to calculate the enthalpy change of a chemical reaction which is not possible by direct experiment and also for those reactions which take place very slowly.

Bond energy. Bond energy of a particular type of bond is defined as the amount of energy required to dissociate or break one mole of that type present in the compound and separate the resulting atoms or radicals from one another.

1. The bond energy of a diatomic molecule is equal to its bond dissociation energy.

Various factors on which bond energy depends are:

(*i*) *Size of atoms.* Smaller the size, greater is the bond energy.

(ii) *Electronegativity.* More the difference in electronegativity values of atoms across a bond, higher will be the numerical value of bond energy.

(iii) *Bond length.* Shorter the bond length, higher is the bond energy.

Spontaneous process. The spontaneous processes are those which take place without external interference of any kind, *e.g.*,

(i) Expansion of a gas into vacuum or in a region of lower pressure from a region of higher pressure.

(ii) Conduction of heat along a metal bar.

(iii) Diffusion of gas into another gas.

Entropy (S). Entropy of a system is a measure of its disorder or randomness. It is denoted by S. The change in entropy (ΔS) is given by

$$\Delta S = S_{final} - S_{initial}$$

For a reversible process taking place under equilibrium condition

$$\Delta S = \frac{Q}{T}$$

$$= \frac{\Delta E + P\Delta V}{T}$$

For irreversible or spontaneous process

$$\Delta S > \frac{\Delta E + P\Delta V}{T}$$

or, $\Delta S > 0$ (*i.e.*/Positive)

Hence spontaneous process occur with increase of entropy.

Unit of Entropy. Joules/Kelvin

- At absolute zero entropy of all pure elements and compounds is zero.
- The entropy of a substance is maximum in gaseous and minimum in solid state.
- More the volume of a given substances more will be its entropy.
- The entropies of impure substances are more than those of pure substances.

- An increase in temperature of a system results in an increase of its entropy.
- The entropy of a real crystal is more than that of an ideal crystal.
- The entropy of poly atomic molecules is more than that of a monoatomic molecule.

Conditions for spontaneous occurrence of a reaction

1. Total change in entropy should be positive.
2. In case of isolated systems ΔS should be positive.

Second law of thermodynamics. It states,

1. The total entropy change for a spontaneous process must always be positive.
2. The entropy of universe always increases.
3. A spontaneous change leads to more disorder.
4. The entropy of a system is maximum when it is in equilibrium state.

Phase transformation. The change of matter from one state (solid, liquid, gas) to another is called phase transformation.

Phase transformation occurs at definite temperature (m.p.; b.p; sublimation temp. etc.).

Entropy of fusion. The fusion of a substance occurs at a definite temp, (*i.e.*, its m.p.) and is accompanied by absorption of heat (*enthalpy of fusion*). The change in entropy known as entropy of fusion is given by

$$\Delta S_{fus} = \frac{\Delta H_{fus}}{T_f}$$

Entropy of vapourisation (ΔS_{vap}). The vapourisation of a substance occurs at a definite temp. (*i.e.*, its b.p) and is accompanied by absorption of heat (*enthalpy of vapourisation*). The change in entropy known as entropy of vapourisation is given by

$$\Delta S_{vap} = \frac{\Delta H_{vap}}{T_b}$$

Rudolf Clausius Summary of First and Second law of thermodynamics

The energy of the universe remains constant but the entropy of the universe tends towards maximum.

Free energy (G). It is the maximum amount of energy available to a system that can be converted into useful work.

It is a measure of the capacity of the system to do the useful work

$$\Delta G = - W_{useful}$$
$$G = H - TS$$

Change in free energy (ΔG)

$$\Delta G = DH - T D S$$

This equation is known as *Gibbs-Helmholtz equation*

- For a spontaneous process ΔG is negative.
- At equilibrium ΔG is zero.

Standard free energy change ($\Delta G°$). It is the free energy change for a process at 298 K when the reactants and products are in their standard state.

$$\Delta G° = \Delta H° - T \Delta S°$$

- The standard free energy of formation ($\Delta G°_f$) of an element in standard state is zero.

Relation between standard free energy change ($\Delta G°$) and equilibrium constant K

$$\Delta G° = - 2.303 \, RT \log k.$$

Change in free energy and electric work

$$\Delta G° = - nFE°.$$

Third Law of Thermodynamics

(i) Entropy of a solid or a liquid approaches zero at absolute zero of temperature.

(ii) Every substance has a finite entropy but at absolute zero temperature the entropy may become zero and it becomes in case of perfectly crystalline solids.

Rate of a reaction. It is defined as the rate of change of concentration of either reactant or product per unit time.

Average rate of reaction. The average rate of reaction can be obtained by dividing the total change in concentration of reactant or product by the elapsed time.

$$\text{Average rate} = \frac{\Delta x}{\Delta t}.$$

Instantaneous rate of a reaction. It is the rate of a reaction when the average rate is taken over a very small interval of time.

Instantaneous rate = Average rate as Δt approaches zero.

Relative rate of a reaction. To get only one numerical value for all the rate expressions for a particular reaction at any given time *we have to divide the rate equation by the coefficient of the reactant or product in the balanced chemical equation.*

Factors that affect the rate of a reaction

- (i) Nature of reactants
- (ii) Concentration of reactants
- (iii) Temperature of reaction
- (iv) Pressure
- (v) Presence of a catalyst
- (vi) Surface area
- (vii) Radiation.

Rate Law or Rate Equation. It is the expression which relates the rate of reaction with concentration of reactants.

rate = $k \times$ [concentration of reactant].

Rate constant. It is the proportionally constant used in the rate equation for the reaction. It is also called *specific reaction rate.*

It is represented by **K** and is equal to the reaction velocity when the molar concentration of each reacting species is unity.

Rate constant is independent of the concentration of reactants but it depends upon the temperature.

Rate constant is a measure of the intrinsic rate of a reaction.

The unit of rate constant is sec^{-1}.

2.4   Oxidation and Reduction

Oxidation is a process in which an atom or a group of atoms taking part in a chemical reaction loses one or more electrons *e.g.*,

$$MnO_4^{-2} \longrightarrow MnO_4^- + e^-$$

$$Fe^{2+} \longrightarrow Fe^{3+} + e^-$$

$$Cu \longrightarrow Cu^{2+} + e^-$$

Reduction is a process in which an atom or a group of atoms taking part in a chemical reaction gains one or more electrons *e.g.*,

$$Ag^+ + e^- \longrightarrow Ag$$

$$Fe^3 + e^- \longrightarrow Fe^{2+}$$

$$[Fe(CN)_6]^{3-} + e^- \longrightarrow [Fe(CN)_6]^{4-}Ag^+ + e^-$$

Any reaction in which both **oxidation** and **reduction** occur simultaneously is known as **Redox reaction** *e.g.*,

$$2Mg \, Cs1 + O_2 \, (g) \longrightarrow 2 \, Mg \, O(s)$$

$$\left\{ \begin{array}{rcll} 2Mg(s) & \longrightarrow & 2Mg^{2+} + 4e^- & (\text{Oxidation}) \\ O_2(g) + 4e^- & \longrightarrow & 2O^{2-} & (\text{Reduction}) \end{array} \right\}$$

Oxidizing agent is the species which can gain electrons during the reaction

$$Cl_2 + 2e^- \longrightarrow 2cl^-$$

Reducing agent is the species that can lose electrons during the reaction

$$Na \longrightarrow Na^+ + e^-$$

In the reaction

$$2K + Cl_2 \longrightarrow 2kCl$$

K (Potassium) acts as reducing agent ($K \rightarrow K^+ + e^-$) and Cl_2 (chlorine) acts as oxidizing agent ($Cl_2 + 2e^- \rightarrow 2Cl^-$)

Oxidation Number

In order to keep track of electron shifts in oxidation-reduction reactions, it is convenient to use the concept of **oxidation number** or **oxidation state** of various atoms involved in oxidation-reduction reactions. *The oxidation number is defined as the formal charge which an atom appears to have when electrons are counted* in accordance with the following rather arbitrary rules.

Rules for Calculating Oxidation Number

(a) *Electrons shared between two unlike atoms are counted with more electronegative atom.* For example, the electron pair shared

between H and Cl in $\overset{+1}{H} : \overset{-1}{\underset{\cdot\cdot}{Cl}} :$ is counted with more electronegative Cl. As a result of it hydrogen having lost share in the electron pair appears to have +1 charge and chlorine appears to have −1 charge, *i.e.*, formal charges of H and Cl are +1 and −1 respectively. Hence oxidation numbers of H and Cl are +1 and −1 respectively.

(b) *Electrons shared between two like atoms are divided equally between the two sharing atoms.* For example, in hydrogen molecule H : H, the electron pair is equally shared between the two atoms. Thus, both the atoms appear to have no charge, *i.e.*, oxidation number of hydrogen is 0 in hydrogen molecule. In the molecule of water given in the margin, the two electron pairs shared between oxygen and the two hydrogen atoms are counted with the more electronegative oxygen atom. Hence in water oxidation number of each H is +1 and that of the O atom is −2.

$$\overset{+1}{H} : \overset{-2}{\underset{\cdot\cdot}{O}} : \overset{+1}{H}$$

Water molecule

(c)   Rules for determining oxidation number. Counting of electrons like this is very laborious.

The following operational rules derived from the above will be found very convenient:

1.   In the elementary or uncombined state, the atoms are assigned an oxidation number of zero.

2.   In compounds, the oxidation number of fluorine is always -1.

3.   In compounds, the group 1 elements (Li, Na, K, Rb, Cs and Fr) have an oxidation number $+1$ and the group 2 elements (Be, Mg, Ca, Sr, Ba and Ra) have an oxidation number $+2$.

4.   Oxidation number of hydrogen in compounds is generally $+1$ except in metallic hydrides wherein its oxidation number is -1.

5.   In compounds, the oxidation number of oxygen is generally -2 except in F_2O wherein oxidation number of fluorine is -1 and that of oxygen is $+2$. in hydrogen peroxide molecule the electron pair shared between O and H is counted with O but the other electron pair shared between two O atoms is equally shared. The number of electrons counted with each O is, therefore, seven (i.e. one more than its own electrons). The oxygen atom therefore appears to have -1 charge or its oxidation number in H_2O_2 is -1.

$$: \overset{..}{O} : \overset{..}{O} :$$
$$\overset{..}{} \quad \overset{..}{}$$
$$H \quad\quad H$$

Hydrogen peroxide

Oxidation and Reduction in term of Oxidation Numbers. The term **Oxidation** *refers to any chemical change involving increase in oxidation number* whereas the term **reduction** *applies to any chemical change involving decrease in oxidation number.*

Consider the following chemical changes:

(i) $2H_2 + O_2 \rightarrow 2H_2O$

Here, oxidation number of hydrogen changes from 0 (in H_2) to $+1$ (in H_2O). It is, therefore, a case of oxidation of hydrogen.

(ii)   Sugar ($C_{12}H_{22}O_{11}$) burns to give CO_2 and water. In this oxidation number of carbon increases from 0 (in $C_{12}H_{22}O_{11}$) to +4 in CO_2. The sugar is, therefore, said to have undergone oxidation.

(iii) When oxygen reacts with hydrogen to give water [example (i)] the oxidation number of oxygen decreases from 0 (in O_2) to –2 (in H_2O). It is, therefore, a case of reduction of oxygen.

In the same reaction, oxidation number of hydrogen increases and that of oxygen decreases, *i.e.*, hydrogen undergoes oxidation while oxygen undergoes reduction. Thus, oxidation and reduction occur together. This is because in oxidation and reduction change of oxidation number occurs as a result of the shift of electrons from one atom A to the other B atom which pulls the electrons towards it. As a result of this electron shift oxidation number of A increases and that of B decreases. Oxidation and reduction must, therefore, always occur together.

When oxidation state of an element in a substance is increased it is called reducing agent and when oxidation state (or oxidation number) decreases, the substance is termed the *oxidizing agent*.

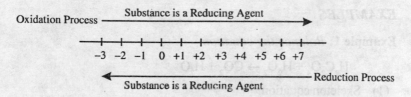

Balancing Chemical Equations Involving Oxidation Reduction. Before a chemical equation can represent correctly a chemical reaction, it must satisfy the following conditions:

(i) It must be chemically correct, *i.e.*, it must be consistent correspond to an actual chemical reaction.

(ii) It must be a *balanced equation*, *i.e.*, it must be consistent with the law of conservation of mass and with the law of conservation of charge.

Balancing is the process of equalizing various atoms on both sides of the equation and equalizing the charge. This is done as under:

(a) **Oxidation Number Method.** The principle underlying this universally applicable method of balancing equations is that electrical charge must be conserved in the course of chemical reaction, *i.e.*, any increase in oxidation number must be compensated by a decrease.

(b) **The Ion-Electrons Method (By use of half-reactions).** In this method the reaction is split up into two half-reactions. In one half-reaction the (i) reducing agent is oxidized and supplies electrons, and in the other half the oxidizing agent picks up electrons and gets reduced. The two half-reactions are balanced separately and added in such a way that the electrons released on the left of one reaction and captured on the right of the other reaction cancel out.

(c) In these reactions electrons are produced during oxidation of the reducing agent and captured by the oxidizing agent which, in turn, is reduced. In fact, galvanic cells are constructed on this basis in which electrons are made to travel from anode where oxidation takes place (*i.e.*, electrons are released) to the cathode where electrons are captured or reduction takes place.

EXAMPLES

Example 1: *Balance the equation*

$$H_2C_2O_4 + H_2O_2 \rightarrow CO_2 + H_2O$$

(1) Skeleton equation:

$$H_2C_2^{+3}O_4 + H_2O_2 \rightarrow CO_2 + H_2O$$

(2) In this reaction oxalic acid is reducing agent, C being oxidized from +3 state to +4 state in CO_2 and H_2O_2 is oxidizing agent, O being reduced from –1 state to –2 state in H_2O.

(3) Writing half-reaction for the oxidation of oxalic acid.
Balancing (i) the atoms in the order carbon-oxygen-hydrogen and in (ii) Equalizing the charge:

$$H_2C_2O_4 \rightarrow 2CO_2 + 2H^+ + 2e^- \qquad \qquad ...(1)$$

(4) Writing the half-reaction for the reduction of H_2O_2:
Balancing (1) the atoms in the order oxygen-hydrogen and

(ii) Equalizing the charge :

$$H_2O_2 + 2H^+ + 2e^- \rightarrow 2H_2O \qquad \ldots(2)$$

(5) Adding up (1) and (2):

$$H_2C_2O_4 + H_2O_2 \rightarrow 2CO_2 + 2H_2O$$

Example 2: *Write a complete balanced equation for the change*

$$Cr_2O_7^{2+} + H_2SO_3 \rightarrow Cr^{3+} + HSO_4$$

taking place in acidic solution.

(1) Writing skeleton equation with oxidation numbers of chromium and sulphur—

Oxidation Numbers

Skeleton: $\overset{+6}{C}r_2O_7^{2-} + H_2\overset{+4}{S}O_2 \rightarrow \overset{+2}{C}r^2 + \overset{+5}{H}SO4^- \qquad \ldots(i)$

(2) *Selecting oxidizing agent and reducing agent.*

Oxidation number of Cr decreases from +6 in $Cr_2O_7^{2-}$ to +3 in Cr^{3+}, it is an oxidizing agent.

Oxidation number of S is raised from +4 in H_2SO_3 to +6 in HSO_4^-, so it is a reducing agent.

(3) Writing half reaction for the oxidation of H_2SO_3, balancing (i) *the atoms in the order* sulphur-oxygen (ii) equalizing the charge by e's on L.H.S.

$$H_2SO_3 + H_2O \rightarrow HSO_4^- + 3H^+ + 2e^- \qquad \ldots(1)$$

(4) Writing half reaction for reduction of Cr_2O_7, balancing (i) the atoms in order of Cr, O, H and equalizing the charge by adding e's on right hand side

$$Cr_2O_7^{2-} + 14H^+ + 6e^- \rightarrow 2Cr^{3+} + 7H_2O \qquad \ldots(2)$$

(5) *Adding the two half reactions*: Multiplying (1) by 3 and adding in order to equalize the number of electrons released in (1) and captured in (2) and adding, we get

$$3H_2SO_3 + Cr_2O_7^{2-} + 5H^+ \rightarrow 3HSO_4^- + 2Cr^{3+} + 4H_2O$$

Example 3: *Balance the equation*

$$H^+ + MnO_4^- + Fe^{2+} \rightarrow Fe^{2+} + Mn^{2+}$$

Solution:

Writing in a similar manner the half-reaction for the reducing agent into an oxidized form:

$$Fe^{2+} \rightarrow Fe^{3+} + e^- \qquad \qquad \dots(1)$$

(1) Writing down the reactant and product of the half-reaction for the oxidizing agent changing into its reduced form balancing (i) the oxygen atoms by adding $4H_2O$ on the right; (ii) adding $8H^+$ on the left; and (iii) Equalizing charge by adding 5 electrons on the left:

$$MnO_4^- + 8H^+ + 5e^- \rightarrow Mn^2 + 4H_2O \qquad \dots(2)$$

Multiplying half-reaction (1) by 5 and adding up to (2), we obtain:

$$MnO_4^- + 8H^+ + 5Fe^{2+} \rightarrow Mn^{2+} \; 5Fe^{2+} + 4H_2O$$

(*Note:* It is more appropriate to use OH^- rather than H^+ in case of alkaline solution)

$$Al(s) + 4OH^- \rightarrow Al(OH)_4^- + 3e^-$$

and $2H_2O + 2e^- \rightarrow 2OH^- + H_2$

These may be combined in appropriate properties (two or three) to give

$$2Al(s) + 2OH^- + 6H_2O \rightarrow 2[Al(OH)_4]^- + 3H_2$$

A particular advantage of *half-reaction* approach is that it leads naturally to the discussion of the thermodynamics of redox reactions in terms of **electrode potential.**

Extraction of the Elements. Since most of the elements occur in combined state, some in positive oxidation state and some in negative oxidation state, so their extraction involves redox chemistry which makes use of some oxidizing or reducing agents.

Iron is extracted from haematite (Fe_2O_3) using the following reaction

$$Fe_2O_3 + \frac{3}{2}C \rightarrow 2Fe + \frac{3}{2}CO_2$$

In metallurgy thermodynamic considerations are very important. For the above reaction ΔG (at 25°C) is +151 kJ mol^{-1} so this reaction is not feasible at room temperature. Since it is highly endothermic ($\Delta H = +234$ kJ/mol) so the equilibrium can be shifted in favour of products at higher temperature (according to be Le Chateliers principle). In a blast furnace the reaction above 1000° C, heat being provided by combustion of carbon in air, which is blown through the reaction mixture.

Carbon being cheap is the most commonly used reducing agent in extractive metallurgy.

In those cases where carbon can not be used as reducing agent some other methods are used for reduction.

Various methods of extraction used are listed below:

Method of Extraction	*Elements*
1. Reduction of oxide with C	Si, P, Mn, Fe, Sn
2. Conversion of Sulphide to oxide and then reduction with carbon.	Co, Zn, Pb, Bi
3. Reaction of sulphide with O_2,	Cu, Hg
4. Electrolysis of solution or molten salt	Li, Be, B, F, Na, Ca, Al, Cl, Ni, Cu, Ga, Sr, In, Ba, Lanthanides, Tl
5. Reduction of halides with sodium or some other electropositive metal.	Be, Mg, Si, K, Ti, V, Cr, Rb, Zr, Cs, Lanthanides, Hf, U
6. Reduction of halides or oxides with hydrogen (H_2)	B, Ni, Ge, Mo, Ru, W, Re
7. Oxidation of arion with Cl_2	Br, I.

In **electrolysis,** a redox process with positive ΔG is induced by providing electrical energy. *Reduction* occurs at **cathode** and *oxidation* occurs at **anode.**

2.5 Describing Inorganic Compounds

Empirical Formula. It is the formula of a compound that represents the relative number of atoms of each element present in one molecule of the compound.

Molecular Formula. It is the formula of a compound that gives the actual number of atoms of various elements present in a molecule of the compound.

Molecular Formula = $n \times$ empirical formula

Where n = 1, 2, 3 ....

To write the formula of compounds containing complex ions we make use of square brackets to represent the complex ion e.g., [Ni (NH$_3$)$_6$] Br$_2$. In it [Ni (NH$_3$)$_6$]$^{2+}$ is the complex ions. It indicates that six NH$_3$ are attached directly to Ni. Such complex compounds are called **coordination compounds.**

In case a metallic and non-metallic element are present in a compound, the name of metallic element is always written first.

For compounds between two or more non-metals they are listed in the following order Xe, Kr, B, Ge, Si, C, Sb, As, P, N, H, Te, Se, S, I, Br, Cl, O, F e.g. OF$_2$ is oxygen diflouride, ClO$_2$ is chloride dioxide etc.

Systematic nomenclature is based on following three systems

 (i) Binary names

 (ii) Substitutive names

(iii) Coordination names.

(i) Binary names

Examples

NaCl	–	Sodium chloride
PCl$_3$	–	Phosphorus trichloride
N$_2$O$_4$	–	Dinitrogen tetroxide
MnO$_2$	–	Manganes (iv) oxide
CsAu	–	Cesium auride
MH$_4$Cl	–	Ammonium chloride

NaCN   –   Sodium cyanide

$Mg\,SO_4$ –   Magnesium sulphate

(ii) Substitutive names

This system is more common in organic chemistry

CH_2Cl_2 –   Dichloromethane (CH_4 is called methane)

SiH_3Cl –   Chlorosilane (SiH_4 is called silane)

$SiCl_4$ –   Tetrachlorosilane

NH_2OH –   Hydroxylamine

(iii) Coordination names

This system is used for complex compounds.

As the co-ordination compounds (or complexes) can be sufficiently complicated, a few formal rules were suggested by the IUPAC to name these compounds. These rules are as stated below:

1. Order of naming ions. *If the compound is ionic, the name of cation is mentioned first followed by the name of anion.* For example,

In the complex $K_2[PtCl_6]$, *the name of cation, potassium is written first followed by the name of anion* $[PtCl_6]^{2-}$ *i.e., hexachloroplatinate (IV).*

Similarly, in the complex $[Co(NH_3)_5Cl]Cl_2$, the name of complex part, $[Co(NH_3)_5Cl]^{2+}$ penta-ammine-chlorocobalt (III) is written first followed by name of anion, Cl^- *i.e.*, chloride.

For the *non-ionic complexes like* $[Ni(NH_3)_4Cl_2]$ *the name of complex is written in one word i.e., tetraammine dichloronickel (II).*

2. Naming of Co-ordination sphere. *In naming the complex, the names of the ligands are written first followed by the name of the central ion. The oxidation number of the central metal atom is expressed by Roman numeral in parentheses just after the name of the central metal atom. The sequence of naming co-ordination sphere is summed up as:*

$$\left(\begin{array}{c}name\ of\\ligands\end{array}\right)\left(\begin{array}{c}name\ of\ central\\metal\ atom\end{array}\right)\left(\begin{array}{c}oxidation\ number\ of\ metal\\in\ Roman\ numeral\end{array}\right)$$

For example in the complex ion, $[Co(NH_3)_6]^{3+}$, the coordination sphere is named as **Hexa-amminecobalt(III) ion.**

Similarly, for the complex ion $[Fe(CN)_6]^{3-}$, the coordination sphere is named as **Hexacyanoferrate(III) ion.**

3. Naming of Ligands. The central metal ion in a complex is surrounded by positive or negative or neutral ligands.

(a) *For the ligands carrying a negative charge the name has a characteristic ending word "O".* A few examples are quoted below:

CH_3COO^- Acetato	NCS^- Isothiocyanato	N^{3-} Nitrido
NH_2^- Amido	NO_2^- Nitro	S^{2-} Sulphido
Cl^- Chloro	O^{2-} Oxo	
CN^- Cyano	O_2^{2-} Peroxo	
CO_3^{2-} Carbonato	$C_2O_4^{2-}$ Oxalato	
OH^- hydroxo	SO_4^{2-} Sulphato	
NH^{2-} Imido	SCN^- Thiocyanato	

(b) *For the ligands carrying a positive charge, the name of the ligand has a characteristics ending of "ium".* For example,

NO_2^+ Nitronium $[NH_2NH_3]^+$ Hydrazinium
NO^+ Nitrosomium.

(c) *For neutral ligands no characteristic ending is used.* For example,

$NH_2CH_2CH_2NH_2$ Ethylenediamine
C_5H_5N Pyridine

The following examples are, however, exceptions:

H_2O Aquo.*   NO Nitrosyl,
NH_3 Ammine,   CO Carbonyl.

(e) *For organic ligands, their names are used as such.* For example,

C_6H_5 Phenyl H_2NCSNH_2 Thiourea
C_5H_5N Pyridine
$P(C_6H_5)_3$ Triphenylphosphine

---

*H_2O is also named as **aqua** these days.

4. Order of naming ligands. According to *old conventions*, the names of more than one type of ligands surrounding the central atom are written in the order, (i) *Negative* (ii) *Neutral* (iii) *Positive*, without separating them with a hyphen. For the ligands of the same kind present in the co-ordination sphere, the names are written in order of their complexity or alphabetical order. For example, in the complex, $[Co(NH_3)_4 Cl(NO_2)]Cl$, the ligands are named in the order chloro, nitro (negative ligands) and ammine (neutral ligand). Thus, the complex $[Co(NH_3)_4 Cl(NO_2)]Cl$ is named as **chloronitrotetra amminecobalt(III) chloride.**

According to the latest **IUPAC Convention** the *names of ligands surrounding the central metal atom are written in alphabetical order of preference irrespective of whether they are negative or neutral.* For example, in the complex $[Co(NH_3)_4 Cl(NO_2)]$, the ligands are named in the order ammine, chloro and nitro. *It must be noted that the prefixes di, tri, etc. are not be considered while determining the alphabetical order.*

In the present text the **new** *IUPAC system has been followed.*

5. Numerical prefixes to indicate number of ligands. The number of each kind of ligands are specified by the prefixes *di, tri, tetra,* etc. If the ligand is complex, such as ethylenediamine (en), ethylenediaminetetra-acetato (edta), etc. and is repeated two, three or four times then the words *bis, tris, tetrakis,* etc., are used followed by the name of the ligand in parentheses. It is illustrated by the examples below:

$[Co(en)_3]Cl_3$ is named as

Tris(ethylenediamine) cobalt(III) chloride

$[Co(H_2NCH_2CH_2NHCH_2CH_2NH_2)_2](NO_3)_3$ is named as

Bis(diethylene triamine) cobalt(III) nitrate

However, when monodentate ligands like methylamine are repeated, the word bis is used instead of **di**. It is because if di is used, it becomes dimethylamine which is a different compound.

6. Ending of name. *Names of complex cations and neutral molecules have no distinguishing termination but in the case of anionic complexes the suffix* **"ate"** *is attached to the name of central* *atom.* For example, the names of some compounds with anionic complexes are:

$K_4[Ni(CN)_4]$ is named as **Potassium tetracyanonickelate(0).**

$Na_3[Co(ox)_3]$ is named as **Sodium tris(oxalato) cobaltate(III).**

$K_3[Fe(CN)_6]$ is named as **Potassium hexacyanoferrate (III).**

7. Naming of bridging groups. For polynuclear complexes *i.e.*, containing two or more metal atoms, the ligands binding two metal atoms are *bridging ligands*. In naming of such ligands the word μ (mu) is added before the name of such ligands and is separated from the rest of the complex by hyphen (-). For more than one bridging group, the word μ is repeated before each bridging group. For example,

$$\left[(en)_2 Co \diagdown \diagup^{NH}_{OH} \diagup \diagdown Co\,(en)_2 \right]^{3+} \text{ is named as}$$

Bis(ethylenediamine)cobalt(III)-μ-imido-μ-hydroxo bis(ethylenediamine)cobalt(III) ion

$$\left[(NH_3)_4 Co \diagdown \diagup^{NH_2}_{NO_2} \diagup \diagdown Co\,(NH_3)_4 \right]^{3+} (NO_3)_4 \text{ is named as}$$

Tetraamminecobalt(III)-μ-amido-μ-nitrotetraamminecobalt(III) nitrate.

The names of some co-ordination compounds on the basis of these rules are given below:

Formula	Name
$Ni(CO)_4$	Tetracarbonylnickel (0)
$[Co(NH_3)_6]Cl_3$	Hexaamminecobalt(III) chloride
$[Co(NH_3)_5Cl]Cl_2$	Pentaamminechlorocobalt(III) chloride
$[Cr(H_2O)_4Cl_2]Cl$	Tetraaquodichlorochromium(III) chloride
$K_4[Ni(CN)_4]$	Potassium tetracyanonickelate(0)
$[Co(NH_3)_3(NO_2)_3]$	Triamminetrinitrocobalt(III)
$[Pt(NH_3)_6]Cl_4$	Hexaammineplatinum(IV) chloride
$K_3[Fe(CN)_6]$	Potassium hexacyanoferrate(III)

Formula	Name
$[Cr(H_2O)_3(NH_3)_3]Cl_3$	Triamminetriaquochromium(III) chloride
$[Pt(NH_3)_2Cl_2]$	Diamminedichloroplatinum(II)
$K_3[Fe(C_2O_4)_3]$	Potassium tris(oxalato) ferrate(III)
$[Co(NH_3)_5CO_3]Cl$	Pentaamminecarbonatocobalt(III) chloride
$[Ag(NH_3)_2]Cl$	Diamminesilver(I) chloride
$[Co(en)_2Cl_2]_2SO_4$	Dichlorobis(ethylenediamine) cobalt (III) sulphate
$[Co(NH_3)_4(NO_2)Cl]NO_3$	Tetraamminechloronitrocobalt(III) nitrate
$K_3[Ir(C_2O_4)_3]$	Potassium trioxalatoiridate(II)
$Hg(Co(SCN)_4]$	Mercuric tetrathiocyanatocobaltate(II)
$\overset{IV}{[Pt(NH_3)_4Cl_2]} \ \overset{II}{[PtCl_4]}$	Tetraamminedichloropaltinum(IV) tetrachloroplatinate(II)
$Na_2[CrOF_4]$	Sodium tetrafluorooxochromate(IV)
$K[BF_4]$	Potassium tetrafluoroborate(III)
$K_2[OsCl_5N]$	Potassium pentachloronitridoosmate(VI)
$[Co(en)_2F_2]ClO_4$	Bis(ethylenediammine) difluorocobalt(III) perchlorate.
$[Co(NH_3)_4Cl_2]_3[Cr(CN)_6]$	Tetraamminedichlorcobalt(III) hexacyanochromate(III)
$[Ag(NH_3)_2]_2SO_4$	Diamminesilver(I) sulphate
$Fe_4[Fe(CN)_6]_3$	Ferric hexacyanoferrate(III)
$[(NH_3)_5Cr{-}OH{-}Cr(NH_3)_5]Cl_5$	Pentaamminechromium(III) -μ-hydroxopentaamminechromium(III) chloride
$Na_2[SiF_6]$	Sodium hexafluorosilicate(IV)
$(C_6H_5)_3P{\Large>}Pd{\Large<}\!\!{\begin{smallmatrix}Cl\\ Cl\end{smallmatrix}}\!\!{\Large>}Pd{\Large<}\!\!{\begin{smallmatrix}Cl\\ P(C_6H_5)_3\end{smallmatrix}}$	Chlorotriphenylphosphine palladium(II) -μ-dichloro chlorotriphenyl phosphine palladium(II)
$[Mn_3(CO)_{12}]$	Dodecacarbonyltrimanganese(0)

(Contd.)

Formula	Name
$[Fe(C_5H_5)_2]$	Bis(cyclopentadienyl) iron (II)
$[Pt(py)_1][PtCl_4]$	Tetrapyridineplatinate(II) tetrachloroplatinate(II)
$Cr(C_6H_6)_2$	Bis(benzene) chromium (O)
$Na_3[Ag(S_2O_3)_2]$	Sodium bis(thiosulphate) argentate(I)
$Li(AlH_4)$	Lithium tetrahydridoaluminate(III)

Structure and Bonding

The complete description of a chemical structure involves specifying the relative coordinates o0f the atoms present or alternatively giving all **bond lengths** and bond angles.

Following terms are commonly used in case of coordination compounds.

Coordination number. The number of ligands directly bonded to the central metal ion in definite geometric patterns is the coordination number of the metal ion.

Primary coordination sphere. The metal ion and the ligands attached to it is called primary coordination sphere. In $K_4[Fe(CN)_6]$, $[Fe(CN)_6]^{4-}$ represents coordination sphere.

Counter ions. The ions which are not included in the primary coordination sphere are known as counter ions *e.g.*, in $K_4[Fe)CN)_6]$, K^+ ions are counter ions.

Primary linkages. Those linkages of the metals which are ionisable are called **primary linkage**s. Such linkages can be satisfied by negative ions.

Secondary linkages. The non-ionisable linkages of the metal are called **secondary linkages**. They can be satisfied by negative ions or neutral groups. The secondary linkages are directed in space about the central metal ion and they provide a structure to the species.

Monodentate ligands. Those ligands in which only one donor atom us bonded to the metal ion are called monodentate ligands *e.g.*, H_2O, NH_3, CO, CO^- etc.

Bidentate ligands. Those ligands which contain two donor atoms or ions through which they are bonded to the metal ions are called bidentate ligands *e.g.*, ethylenediamine (en), oxalate (ox).

Chelate (cyclic complex). An inorganic metal complex having a close ring of atoms formed by attachment of ligands to a metal atom at two points, *e.g.*,

$$\left[\begin{array}{c} H_2C-NH_2 \\ | \\ H_2C-NH_2 \end{array} \begin{array}{c} \\ Cu \\ \end{array} \begin{array}{c} H_2N-H_2C \\ | \\ H_2N-H_2C \end{array}\right]^{2+}$$

Describing bonding in consistent way is much harder. The term **valency** is useful in simple compounds. Valency means the number of bonds formed by an atom. However this idea may be misleading in a number of cases.

In inorganic compounds now the term **oxidation state** is used because it is defined by clearer rules than valency.

3

Structure and Bonding in Molecules

3.1 Electron Pair Bonds

The modern concept of bond between two atoms is some sort of attraction which keeps the two atoms together. Thus a variety of chemical bonds results from the variety of forces which hold the two atoms together in a molecule. Various concepts will be discussed in this chapter.

The Lewis and Langnuir Concept of Stable Configuration

Lewis and Langnuir were the first to recognize the significance of stable octet (*i.e.* 8 electrons in their outermost orbit) as was observed in case of noble gases. All noble gases (except He) have eight electrons in their outermost orbit.

Since the octet and the pair are so stable in noble gases, one can reasonably suspect that all other elements will strive to achieve these configurations

Lewis Symbol or Electron Dot Symbol

Such a symbol marks the number of electrons in the outermost shell of the element around the symbol of the element: *e.g.*

Hydrogen   —   H·

Helium   —   ·He·

Chlorine — $\cdot\ddot{\underset{..}{Cl}}:$

In such symbols inner electrons are not shown.

In case of Lewis symbols for molecules or complex ions similar representation shows the disposition of **valence electrons** around each atom *e.g.*

$$\begin{matrix} H \\ \overset{\cdot\times}{H\times C\times H} \\ \underset{\cdot\times}{} \\ H \end{matrix} \qquad H\overset{..}{\times}\overset{}{O}\overset{..}{\times}H \qquad \overset{\times\times}{\underset{\times\times}{O}}\overset{\times\times}{\times}\overset{\times\times}{\underset{\times\times}{O}} \qquad \overset{\times}{\underset{\times}{N}}\overset{\times}{\underset{\times}{}}\overset{\times}{\underset{\times}{N}}\overset{\times}{\underset{\times}{}}$$

$$\text{(CH}_4) \qquad\qquad \text{(H}_2\text{O)} \qquad\qquad \text{(O}_2) \qquad\qquad \text{(N}_2)$$

These representations are equivalent to the following

$$\begin{matrix} H \\ | \\ H-C-H \\ | \\ H \end{matrix} \qquad H-\overset{..}{\underset{..}{O}}-H \qquad \overset{..}{\underset{..}{O}} = \overset{..}{\underset{..}{O}} \qquad :N \equiv N:$$

$$\text{(CH}_4) \qquad\qquad \text{(H}_2\text{O)} \qquad\qquad \text{(O}_2) \qquad\qquad \text{(N}_2)$$

In these the shared pair of electrons is shown by a line and the **non-bonding** electrons are shown as the atoms.

A molecule of H_2O has **non-bonding** or **lane pair** of electrons present an oxygen atom. The presence of such lane pair has important effect as shape of the molecule and also on its properties.

It is possible to draw complex ions in a similar way *e.g.*

$$\left[\begin{matrix} H \\ | \\ H-N-H \\ | \\ H \end{matrix}\right]^{+} \qquad\qquad \left[\begin{matrix} H \\ | \\ H-B-H \\ | \\ H \end{matrix}\right]^{-}$$

$$\underset{\text{(ammonium ion)}}{\text{(NH}_4^+)} \qquad\qquad \underset{\text{(tetrahydroborate ion)}}{\text{(BH}_4^-)}$$

Octet and Hyper Valency

Octet Rule. Atoms of various elements undergo rearrangements in order to have 8 electrons in their outermost orbit. It is generally referred to as **octet rule** *e.g.* an atom of nitrogen has 5 electrons its valence shell and so must share three more to achieve an octet, thus forming three bonds. Hydrogen is limited to two electrons in its valence shell.

Some molecules containing boron (*e.g.* BF_3) have an incomplete octet (only six electrons with B)

$$
\begin{array}{c}
\overset{\times\times}{\underset{\times\times}{\times}}F \overset{\times}{\underset{\cdot\times}{\times}}B \overset{\times\times}{\underset{\times\times}{\times}}F \overset{\times}{\times} \\
\overset{\times}{\underset{\times\times}{\times}}B \overset{\times}{\times}
\end{array}
$$

and these effect the chemical properties of such compounds.

However structures with complete octets are preferred. Thus a triple bonded carbon monoxide is better than double bonded are

$$: C \equiv O : \qquad\qquad : C = \overset{\cdot\cdot}{\underset{\cdot\cdot}{O}}$$

$$\text{(I)} \qquad\qquad\qquad \text{(II)}$$

In (I) both C and O have 8 electrons.

In (II) carbon fails to complete its octet.

Similarly we have H_2S, H_2Se, H_2Te, H_2O etc. all with completed octets. However some heavier elements can expand their octets (*i.e.* they are capable of **hyper valence** or a valency higher than normal one) *e.g.* in $^SF_4$ and $^SF_6$ the sulphur atom has 10 and 12 electrons in its valence shell.

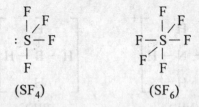

Resonance. Occasionally no reasonable electronic picture can be drawn for a molecule which could satisfactory account for its observed properties. For example, the electronic structure of carbon dioxide may be represented by at least three possible electronic arrangements given below:

$$\ddot{O} \quad C :: O \qquad : \overset{..}{\underset{..}{O}} : C :: \overset{+}{\ddot{O}} : \qquad : \overset{+}{\underset{..}{O}} :: C : \ddot{O} \cdot$$

$$\text{or} \qquad\qquad \text{or} \qquad\qquad \text{or}$$

$$O = C = O \qquad \bar{O} - C \equiv \overset{+}{O} \qquad \overset{+}{O} \equiv C - \bar{O}$$

$$\text{(I)} \qquad\qquad \text{(II)} \qquad\qquad \text{(III)}$$

The calculated heat of formation of carbon dioxide for one formula is 1464 kJ mol^{-1} and the O – O distance should be 2.44Å. However, the observed heat of formation is 1590 kJ mol^{-1} and the O – O distance 2.30Å indicating that none of these structures accounts for its observed properties satisfactorily. This leads to the idea that such compounds exist in a state which is some combination of two or more electronic structures each one of which makes some contribution to its structure.

When several structures may be assumed to contribute to the true structure of a molecule, but no one of them can be said to represent it uniquely, the molecule is referred to as a **resonance hybrid** *and the phenomenon is termed as* **resonance.**

The word resonance for this situation gives us an impression that the molecule resonates from one structure to the other and the electron pair jumps back and fourth from one bond to the other. This is totally wrong and the molecule has only one real electron structure which cannot be physically described. Thus the difficulty lies in the description and not in the molecule itself.

Resonance may also be appropriate with different valence structures that are not equivalent but look equally plausible *e.g.* N$_2$O

$$: \ddot{N} = N = \ddot{O} : \longleftrightarrow :N \equiv N - \overset{..}{\underset{..}{O}} :$$

Formal charges. A formal charge on an atom is essentially the charge that would remain if all covalent bonds are broken, with the electrons being assigned equally to the atoms involved. Thus

Formal charge = (Number of valence electrons in neutral atom)

－ (Number of non-bonding electrons)

－ ½ (Number of bonding electrons)

The formal charge in CO and two valence structures of N_2O are shown below

$$:\overset{-}{C} \equiv \overset{+}{O}: \ , \ :\overset{-}{\overset{..}{N}} = \overset{+}{N} = \overset{..}{O}: \longleftrightarrow :N \equiv \overset{+}{N} - \overset{..}{\overset{..}{O}}:^{-}$$

Thus C^- and O^+ are both isoelectronic to neutral N and can similarly form three bonds.

Formal charges are written in case of organic compounds. They are not always written in case of inorganic compounds.

Formal charge is very different from **oxidation state**, which is assigned by apportioning electrons in a bond to wire electronegative atom rather than equally. Both are artificial assignments.

The concept of resonance is one way of overcoming some limitations of the localised electron pair model.

3.2 Molecular Shapes

VSEPR Principle

The valence shell electron pair repulsion (VSEPR) model is based on the observation that the geometrical arrangement of bonds around an atom is influenced by **non-bonding** electrons present.

Various have been developed and theories put forward to find an answer to the questions like why the molecules acquire a particular shape and what decides the bond lengths, bond angles and bond strength of the bonds that hold atoms in a molecule. One of these is Valence Shell Electron Pair Repulsion Theory **(VSEPR Theory)**.

This theory is applicable to the molecules formed by covalent bonds because these are directional. The force that holds ions together in the ionic compounds is the coulombic force. This force is non-directional and depends on the distance between the ions only. The crystal structure of ionic compound is, therefore, determined by relative sizes and charge of the ions.

The VSEPR theory takes cognition of the facts

1. Covalent bonds are formed by sharing of electrons.

2. Electrons are negatively charged. Therefore all of them (bonding as well as non-bonding) in the valence shells of the bonded atoms in the molecule would strongly repel one another.

To have a stable system, therefore, *according to this theory, only that geometrical arrangement of atoms in a molecule is favoured in which electron pairs are placed as far as possible*. This is illustrated by the following examples.

(a) Molecules in which two electron pairs are shared. Such molecules are of the type *AB*, where two *B* atoms are joined to the central atom *A* each sharing one pair of electrons with *A*. The farthest distance between the shared pair of electrons in the valence shell of *A* in this case, is achieved, when the electrons are placed at an angle of 180°. This AB_2 is linear. Examples of these compounds are beryllium halides, *e.g.*, BeF_2 which has Lewis structure $\left[\ :\overset{..}{\underset{..}{F}}: Be :\overset{..}{\underset{..}{F}}: \ \right]$

(b) Molecules in which three pairs of electrons are shared (AB_3 type). In such molecules the maximum distance between the three shared pairs of electrons (one each by *B* atoms with central atom *A*) is achieved, when these pairs form an equilateral triangular arrangement. Therefore such type of molecules like *boron halides* are planer molecules in which boron-atom is placed at the centre of an equilateral triangle and the three halogen atoms on the three vertices, such that $\angle XBX = 120°$.

For example BCl_3 has the Lewis structure $\left[\begin{array}{c} :\overset{..}{\underset{..}{Cl}}: \ B \ :\overset{..}{\underset{..}{Cl}}: \\ :\overset{..}{\underset{..}{Cl}}: \end{array} \right]$

(c) Molecules in which four pairs of electrons are shared (AB_4 type). In molecules like CH_4 CCl_4, SiI_4, SiF_4, NH_4^+, and BF_4^-, four bonding pairs of electrons are these in the valence shell of the central atoms *A* (one each by *B*). Geometrical arrangement that keeps the shared pairs of electrons as far as possible is the tetrahedral. These molecules are actually known to have tetrahedral shape.

(d) Structure of HF, H_2O and NH_3. Examine the Lewis structures of (i) HF (ii) H_2O and (iii) NH_3 given below

$$\left[\text{H} : \overset{..}{\underset{..}{\text{F}}} : \right] \qquad \left[\overset{..}{\underset{\underset{\text{H}}{|}}{\text{O}}} : \text{H} \right] \qquad \left[\text{H} : \overset{..}{\underset{\underset{\text{H}}{|}}{\text{N}}} : \text{H} \right]$$

(i)   (ii)   (iii)

In all the three molecules, the central atom has four shared pairs of electrons like AB_4 discussed in (c) above. The favourable geometrical arrangement according to VSEPR theory, which keeps the shared pairs of electrons as far as possible, should be tetrahedral like CH_4, CCl_4, etc. But the actual geometry is different which can be easily followed when we look at their Lewis structures given above.

(i)   In the case of HF molecule, there are three non-bonding pairs of electrons and one bonding pair. The two atoms in HF are linearly placed by these bonding electrons, although the four pairs have tetrahedral geometry.

(ii) **H_2O.** In this case out of the four shared pairs of electrons in the valence shell of O atom, two are non-bonding and the other two bonding pairs. The two H-atoms held by bonding pairs are placed at the two corners of the tetrahedron whose other two corners are occupied by the non-bonding electron pairs. The angle $\angle HOH$ in H_2O is predicted to be $109.5°$. Actually this angle is found to be $104.5°$. We shall get the explanation of this discrepancy later. Molecules like F_2O, SCl_2 and ions like NH_2^- have similar shapes.

(iii) **NH_3.** In the molecule of NH_3, N has three bonding and one non-bonding pair of electrons. The three bonding pairs keep the H-atoms at three vertices while the fourth is occupied by the non-bonding pair. NH_3 molecule thus appears like a triangular pyramid in which three H-atoms form an equilateral triangle as the base with N atom at the apex of the pyramid. The $\angle HNH$ is nearly the same as in a tetrahedron, *i.e.*, $109.5°$. The actual angle is $107°$ in this case. The cause of this difference is explained later. Some examples of molecules and ions having this type of structure are PF_3, NCl_3, NF_3, PCl_3 and H_3O^+

   (e) Molecules with five pairs of shared electrons. Molecules like PCl_5 (gas) have five pairs of shared electrons in the valence shell of the central atom (*P* in this case). In accordance with the *VSEPR* theory, *trigonal bipyramidal geometry* is the arrangement in which these shared pairs of electrons are kept as far as possible. These molecules are actually found to have the trigonal bipyramid structure.

(f) Molecules with six pairs of shared electrons. Molecules like SF_6 and ions like PCl_6^- have six pairs of shared electrons in the valence shell of the central atom. In order that the electron pairs around the central atom in the molecule must stay as far apart as possible, the geometrical shape that arises, according to *VSEPR* theory is Octahedral.

Arranagement	Bond angle	Geometry of the molecule formed	Examples
Linear	180°		$BeCl_2$, $HgCl_3$
Trigonal planar	120°	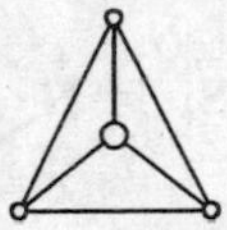	BF_3, BCl_3, NO_3^-
Tetrahedral	109°	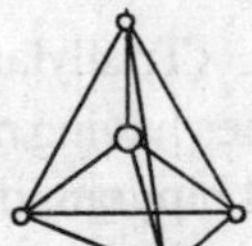	CH_4, NH_4^+
Square planar	90°		$[Ni(CN)_4]^{2-}$, $[PtCl_4]^{2-}$
Trigonal Bipyramid	90° 120°	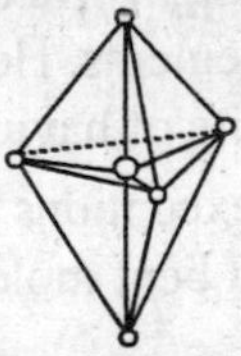	PCl_5, PF_5
Octahedral	90°	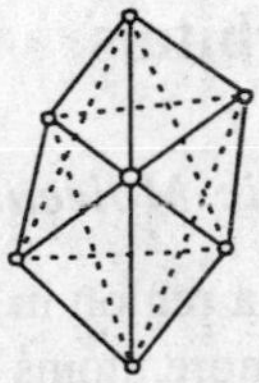	SF_6, $[Ni(NH_3)_6]^{2+}$

Fig. 3.1. Shape of polyatomic molecules, indicated on R.H.S.

VSEPR should be able to predict the geometry around any atom in a complex molecule, where main-group atoms are involved (It can not be generally applied to transition metals) *e.g.,* in NH_2OH, the bonds around the nitrogen are pyramidal and those around oxygen bent as expected.

This model is useful even in interpreting solid-state structures containing ions such as Sr^{2+} where non-bonding electrons appear to have stereochemical influence.

Exception of **VSEPR** arises when apparently non-bonding electrons are really involved to some extent in bonding *e.g.,* geometry around nitrogen is planar when bonded to carbonyl groups in peptide linkage (— NH — C —) in proteins and in trisilylamine, (Si $H_3)_3$ N, which contracts with pyramidal trimethylamine, $(CH_3)_3N$, where the carbon can not accommodate extra electrons.

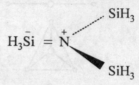

$$H_3\bar{S}i = \overset{+}{N}$$

(Trisilylamine)

Sometimes AX_5 species having no lane pairs are square pyramidal instead of normal trigonal bipyramidal.

Difficulties also arise in case of AX_6 species where there is one non-bonding pair (e.g. XeF_6). XeF_6 is not regularly octahedral, a predicted. A unique shape can not be determined in gas phase, however the molecule seems to be highly **fluxinol** and converts rapidly between different distorted arrangements. However $[SeCl_6]^{2-}$ and $[TeCl_6]^{2-}$ are regularly octahedral inspite of having a non-bonding pair.

Some other notable exceptions are dihalides of group 3 elements *e.g.* BaF_2 (in gas phase, a bent molecule).

3.3 Molecular Orbitals

Homonuclear Diatomic Molecules

Molecular orbital. It is a region in space defined by size and shape associated with two or more atoms in a molecule having a capacity of two electrons.

Sigma (σ-) orbital. A molecular orbital which is symmetrical about a line joining the two nuclei (the bond axis) is called a sigma (σ-) orbital. It may be bonding or anti-bonding molecular orbital.

Pi- (π-) orbital. A molecular orbital which has regions of electronic charge build up or electron density, on directly opposite side of the bond axis is called a π-orbital. It may be bonding or anti-bonding.

LCAO (Linear combination of atomic orbitals). It is simple and qualitative approximation which can explain the formation of molecular orbitals by combination of atomic orbitals.

Bonding molecular orbital. A molecular orbital which is formed by addition overlap of atomic orbitals is known as bonding molecular orbitals.

The energy of a bonding molecular orbital is lower than the combining atomic orbitals. It favours formation of a bond

$$\varphi_{M.O.} = \varphi_A + \varphi_B.$$

Anti-bonding molecular orbitals. A molecular orbital obtained by the subtraction overlap of two atomic orbitals is known as anti-bonding molecular orbital.

The energy of an anti-bonding molecular orbital is higher than those of combining atomic orbitals. It does not favour formation of a bond.

$$\varphi_{M.O.} = \varphi_A + \varphi_B.$$

Energy level diagrams. The diagram that shows the formation of various molecular orbitals from atomic orbitals and the filling of electrons in the molecular orbitals is known as energy level diagram of the molecule.

The **formation of bonding and anti-bonding** orbitals can also be interpreted in terms of sign of wave functions of the orbitals which interact. Since a wave processes a *crest* and *a trough* therefore the *positive* and *negative* signs are arbitrarily assigned to the crest and trough respectively.

In order to understand it let us consider the interference of waves. Now if the crest of one wave overlaps with the crest of the other, the two waves interact in a *constructive interference* and therefore the new resulting wave is *reinforced i.e. add up*. In other words, there is in *phase overlap* or *addition overlap* [Fig 3.1 (a)]. In the similar way, addition overlap of atomic orbitals with same signs leads to the formation of **bonding molecular orbital.** On the contrary, if the crest of one wave overlaps with the trough of the other, then two waves interact in a *destructive* manner. In other words, this is *out of phase overlap* or *subtraction overlap* and the resulting wave is weakened [Fig. 3.1 (b)]. Such type of subtraction overlap of atomic orbitals with opposite signs leads to the formation of **anti-bonding molecular orbital.**

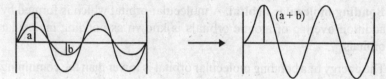

Fig. 3.1. (a) Constructive interference; amplitude are added up.

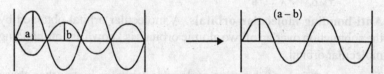

Fig. 3.1. (b) Destructive interference; amplitudes are subtracted.

The combination of $1s$ orbitals of hydrogen atoms to form molecular orbitals has been shown in Fig. 3.2.

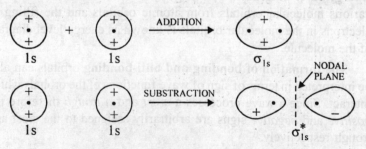

Fig. 3.2. Molecular orbitals formed by the combination of two $1s$ orbitals.

Relative energies of atomic and molecular orbitals in hydrogen molecule are shown in Fig 3.3.

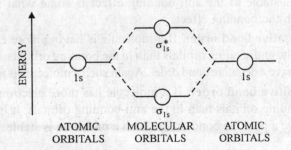

Fig. 3.3. Relative energies of bonding and anti-bonding molecular orbitals.

It may be noted that bonding molecular orbital is stabilized almost to the same extent as the anti-bonding molecular orbital is destabilized relative to atomic orbitals.

M.O. Diagrams

The molecular orbital energy level diagram for Homonuclear diatomnic molecules like H_2, H_2^+, He_2^+, He_2 (hypothetical), Li_2, Be_2 (hypothetical) O_2, F_2, Ne_2 (hypothetical) is given in Fig 3.4 (a).

Bond order. It is defined as half of the difference between number of electrons in bonding and anti-bonding molecular orbitals.

$$\text{Bond order} = \frac{\left(\begin{array}{c}\text{Number of electrons} \\ \text{in bonding molecular} \\ \text{orbitals}\end{array}\right) - \left(\begin{array}{c}\text{Number of electrons} \\ \text{in antibonding} \\ \text{molecular orbitals}\end{array}\right)}{2}$$

It is a measure of the strength of the bond, greater the bond order, greater will be the stability of the molecule. Greater the bond order shorter will be the bond length.

Types of Bond Order

(i) **Zero bond order.** When the number of electrons in the bonding molecular orbitals is equal to the number of electrons in the anti-bonding molecule orbitals, in a molecule, then such a molecule is said to have zero bond order. This type of molecule is unstable as the anti-bonding effect is some what stronger than the bonding effect.

(ii) **Negative bond order.** If a molecule is having more electrons in the antibonding orbitals than in the bonding orbitals, it is said to have a negative bond order. Again such a molecule is unstable.

(iii) **Positive bond order.** If a molecule has more electrons in the bonding orbitals than in the anti-bonding orbitals, it is said to have a positive bond order. Such a molecule is stable.

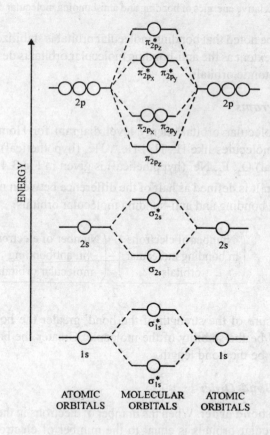

Fig. 3.4. (a) Molecular orbital energy level diagram for diatomic homonuclear molecules such as O_2, F_2, etc.

The following table lists some bond parameters of a few homonuclear diatomic molecules.

Molecule/ Ion	Electronic configuration	Bond	Bond	I.E.
N2	KK $\sigma 2s^2\ \overset{**}{\sigma}2s^2\ \sigma 2p_z^2\ \pi 2p_x^2\ \pi 2p_y^2$	3	110	945
O_2^+	KK $\sigma 2s^2\ \overset{**}{\sigma}2s^2\ \sigma 2p_z^2\ \pi 2p_x^2\ \pi 2p_y^2\ \overset{**}{\pi}2p_x^1$	2.5	112	630
O_2	KK $\sigma 2s^2\ \overset{**}{\sigma}2s^2\ \sigma 2p_z^2\ \pi 2p_x^2\ \pi 2p_y^2\ \overset{**}{\pi}2p_x^2$	2	121	498
O_2^-	KK $\sigma 2s^2\ \overset{**}{\sigma}2s^2\ \sigma 2p_z^2\ \pi 2p_x^2\ \pi 2p_y^2\ \overset{**}{\pi}2p_x^2\ \overset{**}{\pi}2p_y^1$	1.5	128	–
F_2	KK $\sigma 2s^2\ \overset{**}{\sigma}2s^2\ \sigma 2p_z^2\ \pi 2p_x^2\ \pi 2p_y^2\ \overset{**}{\pi}2p_x^2\ \overset{**}{\pi}2p_y^2$	1	142	158

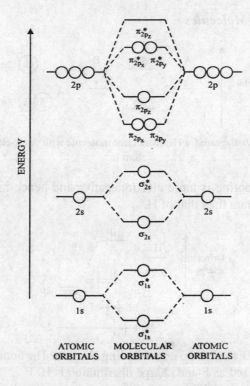

Fig. 3.4. (b) Molecular orbital energy level diagram for diatomic homonuclear molecules such as N_2, C_2, and B_2.

Heteronuclear Diatomic Molecules

In such molecules the molecular orbitals are not shared equally between atoms *e.g.*, in gas phase Li H with $2s$ electrons on Li and $1s$ on H, when M.O's are constructed using LCAO method.

$$\varphi = C_1 \, \phi_1 + C_2 \, \phi_2$$

The coefficients of C_1 and C_2 are no longer equal. In Li H they greatly differ in energy. In bonding M.O. $C_1 > C_2$ and this gives (φ^2) more electron density as the more electronegative atom. As the electronegativity difference between atoms increases so does the delocalisation of M.O. making the charge distribution more ionic.

To illustrate the point we take two molecules **HF** and **BH**.

HF and BF Molecules

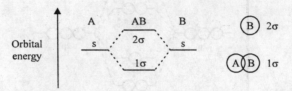

Fig. 3.5. M.O. diagram for Heteronuclear molecule with one s-electron per atom.

In HF, fluorine is more electronegative and hence its AO's are lower in diagram than that of H.

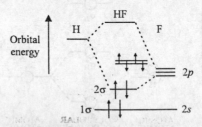

Thus in HF there is no **non-bonding** electron. The bonding orbital is more localised as F and charge distribution is $H^{\delta+}F^{\delta-}$.

In BH the electronegativity difference are reversed and bonding orbitals will be more localized on H. However $2s$ and $\sigma 2p$ A.O.'s on boron are of comparable energy and both can contribute to the bonding. The M.O.'s are formed by $1s$ of H and $2s$ and $2p$ orbitals of Boron of the three M.O.'s formed one is **bonding**, one is **antibonding** and one is approximately **non-bonding.** It can be understood by formation of *sp* **hybrid orbitals** by Boron atom, one of these *sp* **hybrid orbitals** combines with H, $1s$, forming two M.O. (one bonding and one antibonding) and the second *sp* hybrid orbitals, which does not overlap much is **non-bonding.** The four valence electrons in BH thus make a bonding and a non-bonding pair oriented in opposite directions. The bond order is **one** with charge distribution $B^{\delta+} - H^{\delta-}$

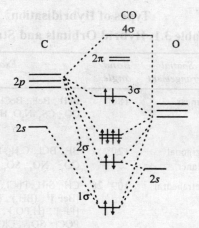

CO Molecule

In CO, there is only one pair of equivalent A.O.'s on each atom. They contribute to the bonding 1π and antibonding 2π M.O.'s. The four M.O. are labelled as 1σ, 2σ, 3σ, and 4σ. In it we can imagine the formation of two *sp* hybrid orbitals on each atom which then overlap to give M.O. 1σ is strongly bonding and 4σ is strongly antibonding.

The other two are non-bonding, with 2σ localised as oxygen and 3σ localised as carbon.

The highest occupied Molecular orbital **(HOMO)** is the carbon 'lane pair' 3σ orbital and the lowest unoccupied molecular orbital **(LUMO)** is antibonding 2π.

The **HOMO** and **LUMO** are called the **frontier orbitals** and can be used to understand the interaction of molecules with other species.

This is useful in understanding the bonding in $Ni\,(CO)_4$.

Polyatomic Molecules

In such molecules alternative bonding description are possible. These may involve either localized (two centre) or delocalised (three or more centres) molecular orbitals. The over all distribution predicted may be the same in both cases.

The localized M.O. lead to directed valence and the shape may depend on type of hybridisation used.

The following table illustrates the point.

Types of Hybridisation
Table 3.1. Hybrid Orbitals and Structures

Hybridisation	Spatial arrangement	Bond angle	Examples
1. sp	Linear	180°	BeH_2, BeF_2, $BeCl_2$, $HgCl_2$, C_2H_2, HCN, CO_2, CS_2, N_2O, Hg_2Cl_2, $[Ag(CN)_2]^-$
2. sp^2	Trigonal planer	120°	BF_3, BCl_3, C_2H_4, $H—\overset{\overset{O}{\|}}{C}—H$, $Cl—C—Cl$, CO_3^{2-}, NO_3^-, SO_3, CH_3, $(CH_3)_3C$
3. sp^3	Tetrahedral	109° 28'	CH_4, SiH_4, $PbCl_4$, $TiBr_4$, CCl_4, SiF_4, $[BeF_4]^{2-}$, $(BH_4)^-$, $[BF_4^-]$, NH_4^+, $[AlCl_4]^-$, $[PF_4]^+$, $[H_2PO_2]^-$, $[HPO_3]^{2-}$, $[PO_4]^{3-}$, $POCl_3$, SO_4^{2-}, ClO_4^-, $Ni(CO)_4$, $[Zn(CN)_4]^{2-}$, $[AsO_4]^{3-}$, $[SeO_4]^{2-}$, $[IO_4]^{2-}$, XeO_4, MnO_4^-, CrO_4^{2-}
4. dsp^2	Square	90°	$[Cu(NH_3)_4]^{2+}$, $[PtCl_4]^{2-}$, $[Ni(CN)_4]^{2-}$, $[PdCl_4]^{2-}$, $[Pt(NH_3)_4]^{2+}$, $[AuCl_4]^-$
5. sp^3d or	Trigonal bipyramidal	120° and 90°	PCl_5, PF_5, AsF_5, $SbCl_5$, XeO_3F_2, $[Fe(CO)_5]$

Hybridisation	Spatial arrangement	Bond angle	Examples
6. sp^3d^2 or d^2sp^3	Octahedral	90°	SF_6, $[PF_6]^-$, $[BiCl_6]^-$, $[PCl_6]^-$, $[AsF_6]^-$, $[SeF_6]$, MoF_6, $[SbCl_6]^-$, TeF_6, WCl_6, UF_6, XeO_2F_4, All six coordinated complexes are octahedral
7. sp^3d	Pentagonal bipyramidal	72°	IF_7, $[ZrF_7]^{3-}$, $[UF_7]^{3-}$, $[UO_2F_5]^{3-}$, SF_7

Table 3.2. Hybridisation and Structure involving lone pair

Hybridisation	Bonded pair	Lone pair	Bond angle	Shape	Example
1. sp^2	2	1	119°	Bent molecule or V-shaped	SO_2, $SnCl_2$, $PbCl_2$
2. sp^3	3	1	107°	Pyramidal	NF_3, PF_3, SO_3^{2-}, XeO_3, ClO_3^-, $P(CH_3)^3$, $N(CH_3)_3$, $AsCl_3$, $BiCl_3$, $SbCl_3$, NH_3, PCl_3, PH_3, (Bond angle 94°)
3. sp^3	2	2	104.5°	V-shape	H_2O, H_2S (Bond angle 92°), SCl_2, OF_2, Cl_2O, H_2Se, NH_2^-, $ClOF$, CH_3OCH_3, ClO_2^-
4. sp^3d	3	2	120° 90°	Trigonal pyramidal	SF_4, SCL_4, $TeBr_4$, $TeCl_4$, XeO_2F_2
5. sp^3d	3	2	90°	T-shaped	ClF_3, $XeOF_2$, IF_3, BrF_3, ICl_3, IBr_3
6. sp^3d	2	3	180°	Linear	XeF_2, I_3^-, ICl_2^-, KrF_2
7. sp^3d^2	5	1	90°	Square pyramidal	ClF_5, $XeOF_4$, IF_5, $(SbF_5)^{2-}$
8. sp^3d^2	4	2	90°	Square planer	XeF_4, ICl_4^-, ClF_4^-
9. sp^3d^3	6	1	~90°	Distorted octahedral	XeF_6

To find the hybrid state of an atom in different species following points be considered.

Predicting the Hybrid State of atom in different species

(i)   Write the valence electrons of Central atom (V)

(ii) Add number of surrounding atoms except oxygen (SA)

(iii) If there is positive charge on species, subtract the charge; if there is –ve charge, add the charge

(iv) Divide the sum by 2 to get value of X.

$$X = \frac{1}{2}(V + SA \pm E)$$

Value of X	2	3	4	5	6	7
Hybrid state of central atom	sp	sp^2	sp^3	sp^3d	sp^3d^2	sp^3d^3

Note. The above formula is not applicable to predict hybrid state of metal in complexes and species having multi-central atoms.

BF_4^-	IF_3	SO^2	I_3^-	SO_4^{2-}	CO_3^{2-}
$\dfrac{3+4+1}{2}=4$	$\dfrac{7+3}{2}=5$	$\dfrac{6}{2}=3$	$\dfrac{7+2+1}{2}=5$	$\dfrac{6+2}{2}=4$	$\dfrac{4+2}{2}=3$
sp^3	sp^3d	sp^2	sp^3d	sp^3	sp^2

Three Centre Bonding

We come across this type of bonding in diborane (B_2H_6)

(Three electron bond)   (bridging hydrogen)

The terminal B–H bonds are simple two electron bonds, but the number of electrons available suggests that each bridging hydrogen forms part of a $3c$ bond involving two boron atoms.

The **three-centre-two electron bond** ($3c2e$) because in addition of B–H overlap there is some direct overlap between the boron hybrids which provides B–B bonding as well.

Such type of bonds occurs in other circumstances *e.g.*, BeH_2, which has a polymeric chain structures with H atoms in the bridging positions.

Other groups such as CH_3 can do this *e.g.* in dimeric aluminium methyl, $Al_2 (CH_3)_6$, which has a structure similar to B_2H_6 with CH_3 in place of H.

Another type of bridging H occurs in symmetrical ions (FHF⁻) formed by hydrogen bonding in F⁻ and HF. It leads to **3c4e model** which are an alternative to use of d-orbitals in hypervalent compounds with octet expansion *e.g.* XeF_2

$$F^- \quad {}^+Xe-F \quad \longleftrightarrow \quad F-Xe^+ \quad F^-$$

3.4 Rings and Clusters

Ring and clusters structures of some molecules can be understood using simple two centre bonds but in some cases we need M.O. (delocalised models) for their understanding.

Rings are generally formed by non-metallic elements with directional covalent bonding *e.g.* S_8, C_6H_6, S_2N_2, $B_3N_3H_6$, $(Si_3O_9)^{3-}$ etc.

(S_8) (N_2S_2) (P_4) (Pb_5)

Clusters are polyhedral arrangements of atoms *e.g.*, P_4 $(Pb_5)^{2-}$

Many **rings** and **clusters**, can not be understood within two centre two electron bond. For understanding some such molecules **Huckel Theory** of ring systems is quite useful. This theory makes important predictions relevant to inorganic molecules such as S_2N_2 **(rings)**.

Clusters (such as boranes) can be understood by M.O.'s on the basis of **Klade's rules** which provide a useful systematization of the principles involved.

Aromatic Rings

The **Huckle M.O. model** predicts that rings will have aromatic stability if they have $(4n + 2)$ delocalised π–electron, where n is a whole number. Inorganic applications include, S_2N_2, which has 6π electrons.

The π electrons of rings such as benzene (C_6H_6) form delocalised molecular orbitals. In case of benzene of the six delocalised M.O. formed, the **lowest energy** M.O is formed by combining all $2p$ orbitals with *positive overlap* to give **full bonding**, higher energy orbitals are progressively less bonding and more antibonding.

Aromatic stability arises because the electrons are collectively more stable in these M.O.'s than they would be in separate double bonds.

The following diagram shows these energies.

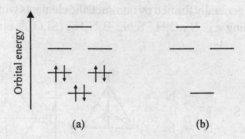

(a)   (b)

Fig. 3.6. Energies of p M.O.'s in (a) benzene (b) four membered ring.

The arrangement of M.O. energies for benzene is paralleled with other ring sizes, in each case there is a single orbital of lowest energy followed by pairs of equal energy.

Since the assignment of 4π electrons does not lead to a closed shell ground state, where every M.O. is either filled or empty, so it is not stable. It is actually so in case of the 4π molecule (*cyclobutadiene*).

On basis of this type of argument we come to Huckel Rule [$(4n + 2)$ rule].

Now we can say why $[C_5H_5]^-$ (cyclopentadienyl) is stable (it has 6π electrons).

The inorganic compound that conform to Huckel's rule are $B_3N_3H_6$, S_2N_2, $[S_4]^{2+}$, $[Se_4]^{2+}$ etc.

Wades Rules

For understanding various structures found in **boranes,** we have to recognize the following families of such compounds.

(i) **Closo boranes.** In them n boron atoms adopt closed polyhedral structures which are based on trigonal bipyramids (five vertices), octahedron (Six) and icosahedron (12). Such polyhedra are called *deltahedra*. Examples of this type are $[B_nH_n]^{2-}$ *i.e.* $[B_6H_6]^{2-}$ etc.

(ii) **Nido boranes (nest like).** In them a boron atoms are found roughly at the position of vertices of $(n + 1)$ vertex deltahedron, with one vertex missing *e.g.*, B_nH_{n+4} *i.e.* B_5H_9 etc.

(iii) **Arachno boranes (web like).** These boranes are still more open and they can be imagined as deltahedra with two vertices missing *e.g.*, B_nH_{n+6} *i.e.* B_4H_{10} etc.

Wade's rules provide an electronic rationalization of the regularities, based on M.O. predictions that an n atom deltahedron, with s- and p- valence orbitals, should have **(n + 1) skeletal bonding M.O.'s** *e.g.* $[B_6H_6]^{2-}$ has 7 such orbitals.

The electrons counting can be done as follows. In $[B_6H_6^{2-}]$ there are 26 valence electrons $(6 \times 3 + 6 \times 1 + 2 = 26)$ of these 12 are assigned to 6 B–H bonds and some are left with 14 **skeletal bonding electrons.** These 14 electrons can not be assigned by any simple method to localized two centre or even three centre bonds. Thus we can say that **closo boranes** with n atoms should have $(2n + 2)$ skeletal bonding electrons.

Similarly we can show that in case of **nido boranes** with n atoms we should have **(2n + 4) skeletal bonding electrons** and in case of **arachno boranes** with n atoms we must have **(2n + 6) skeletal bonding electrons.**

e.g., B_5H_9 (nidoborane) has 14 skeletal bonding electrons.

Wade's rules are applicable to "naked" clusters formed by p-block elements and so in case of $[Pb_5]^{2-}$ having 22 valence electrons we expected 10 used lane pairs and 12 skeletal bonding electrons *i.e.* a **closo** structure.

On similar considerations $[Sn_9]^{4-}$ which has 22 skeletal bonding electrons should possess **nido** structures.

There are exceptance to Wade's rules. Extension to d-block elements needs to accommodate d-bonding electrons and this leads us to **Wades-Mingos rules.**

3.5 Bond Strength

We have already defined the terms bond enthalpy, bond energy etc. Here we will take up important trends observed.

(i) On moving down a group, the bond energy generally decreases (*e.g.* C—H > Si—H > Ge—H etc). A number of exceptions have been observed and the trends reserves in case of transition elements.

(ii) Bond energies increase as the bond order increases. The strong multiple bond formed by C, N, O etc. may be attributed to very efficient overlapping of $2p$-orbitals in comparison to larger orbitals of the lower periods.

(iii) In AB_n type compounds, in case of the same elements with different n values, B(A–B) decreases as n increases (*e.g.* in case of $ClF > ClF_3 > ClF_5$ etc.). The differences are generally less for larger A and more electronegative B.

(iv) Single A – B bonds where A and B both are from the set N, O, F are weaker than expected from group comparison. It is because of *repulsion between non-bonding electrons.*

(v) Bonds are stronger between elements with a large electronegativity difference. (This forms the basis of *Paulings* electronegativity scale).

Pauling Electronegativity

Pauling related the bond strengths to the electronegativity χ_A and χ_B of the two elements as

$$B(A - B) = \sqrt{[B(A - A)B(B - B)]} + C(\chi c_A - \chi_B)^2$$

where C is a constant and its value is 96.5 if B values are in KJ mol^{-1}.

On this scale the electronegativity value of fluorine is 4.

Pauling formula is purely empirical, but it provides a good rationalization of bond strengths and pauling scale is commonly used for estimating unknown enthalpies.

It should not be used for solids with a high degree of ionic character and the lattice energy be used instead.

Uses of Bond energies: It is used:

(i) To estimate the enthalpy of formation of a hypothetical compound.

(ii) To rationalize the trends in stability a structure of related compounds.

In some cases where it is difficult to measure bond energy we make use of **bond length** or **bond stretching frequency** for comparing the bond strengths.

Bond length for a given pair of elements decreases with increase in bond strength. The measurement of bond length is quite useful to show the existence of metal-metal bonds in compounds of transition elements.

Bond stretching frequency (measured by vibrational spectroscopy such IR spectroscopy etc.) is related to **stretching force constant** and increases with increase in bond strengths. This study is quite useful for transition metal carbonyls.

3.6 Lewis Acids and Bases

Lewis Definition of Acids and Bases. An even more generalized theory of acids and bases was put forward by Lewis. According to **Lewis definition** *an acid is a substance that can accept an electron pair to form a covalent bond and base is a substance that can furnish an electron pair to form a covalent bond.* In other words, *an acid is an electron pair acceptor and a base is an electron pair donor.* This is the most general and fundamental of the ACID-BASE concepts and includes all the other concepts.

A proton is an acid since it needs an electron pair to complete its shell. *It is a* **Lewis acid** *or it is an acid in the* **Lewis sense.** Hydroxide ion, ammonia and water are Lewis bases because they contain electron pairs available for sharing.

In reaction between BF_3 and NH_3, boron accepts the lone pair from nitrogen forming a covalent bond.

$$\begin{array}{ccc}
\overset{\displaystyle F}{\underset{\displaystyle F}{|}}\!\!-\!\!B & & \overset{\displaystyle F}{\underset{\displaystyle F}{|}}\!\!-\!\!B \\
\end{array}$$

$$\overset{F}{\underset{F}{\overset{|}{F-B}}} \;+\; :NH_3 \longrightarrow \overset{F}{\underset{F}{\overset{|}{F-B}}}-\overset{+}{N}H_3$$

Acid   Base

The Lewis theory does not differ from Bronsted theory with respect to substances classified as bases. A substance capable of donating an electron pair (*i.e.*, any Lewis base) is capable of donating electron pair to a proton. Being proton acceptor it is also a Bronsted base. Thus both definitions label the following as bases.

$$H-\overset{..}{\underset{..}{O}}{}^- \; ; \quad H-\overset{..}{\underset{..}{O}}-H \; ; \quad :\overset{..}{\underset{..}{Cl}}{}^- \; ; \quad :\overset{..}{\underset{..}{Br}}{}^-$$

$$C_2H_5\overset{..}{\underset{..}{O}}H \; ; \quad C_2H_5O C_2H_5 \; ; \quad :NH_3$$

However, many species which are acids under Lewis definition cannot be termed so according to Bronsted definition. A few examples are sulphur trioxide and halides of boron, aluminium, iron (ferric) and zinc. The central atom in each is able to accept a pair of electrons to complete is octet

$$\overset{..}{\underset{..}{S}}\!:\overset{\displaystyle :\overset{..}{O}:}{\underset{\displaystyle :\overset{..}{O}:}{}}\overset{..}{O}: \qquad \overset{\displaystyle :\overset{..}{X}:}{\underset{\displaystyle :\overset{..}{X}:}{Al::X:}} \qquad \overset{\displaystyle :\overset{..}{X}:}{\underset{\displaystyle :\overset{..}{X}:}{B::X:}} \qquad :\overset{..}{\underset{..}{X}}:Zn:\overset{..}{\underset{..}{X}}:$$

Similarly, in a Bronsted acid like H Cl, there is no vacant orbital to accept an electron pair from a base. There is, therefore, no obvious reason to label it as an acid according to Lewis definition.

Models of Interaction

The scope of donor-acceptor concept is extremely broad and includes interaction such as electrostatic, solvation and complexation of metal ions etc.

Interaction between orbitals will be strongest when the energy difference between the acceptor **LUMO** and the donor **HOMO** is least.

The best acceptor will be empty orbital at low energies and the best donor will be filled orbital at high energies.

However the strongest electrostatic attraction will occur between smallest and most highly charged (positive) acceptor and (negative) donor atoms.

Hard-Soft Classification: The **hard and soft acid-base (HSAB)** classification is used for rationalization of differences, when two acids $(A_1$ and $A_2)$ are competing for two bases $(B_1$ and $B_2)$

$$A_1 B_1 + A_2 B_2 = A_1 B_2 + A_2 B_1$$

The equilibrium will lie in the direction where the **harder** of the two **acids** is in combination with the **harder base** and **softer acid** with **softer base.**

For comparison the prototype **hard acid H^+** and **soft acid** $[(CH_3) Hg]^+$ are generally used.

$$[B : H]^+ + [(CH_3) Hg]^+ = H^+ + [(CH_3) Hg B]^+$$

Equilibrium will lie to the left according to degree of hardness of B.

Hard acids. H^+, cations of very electro-positive metals (Mg^{2+} etc.), non-metal fluorides (BF_3 etc).

Soft acids. Cations of late transition metals and post transition metals (Cn^+, Pd^{2+}, Hg^{2+})

Hardness of Base. It increases with the group number of the donor atom (NH_3 $CH_2O \angle F^-$) and decreases as we move down a group ($NH_3 > PH_3$; F^-) Cl^-) $Br^-)Z^-$).

Soft acceptors and donor atoms are generally large and vander waal's forces may contribute to bonding.

π-acceptor behaviour is shown by some soft bases (*e.g.* CO)

Polymerisation

The tendency to form dimers (*e.g.* Al_2Cl_6) etc., can be considered as donor-acceptor interaction

$$2Al Cl_3 \rightarrow Al_2 Cl_6$$

Polymerisation of AX_n molecules is more likely to occur when n is small, and when the atom A has vacant orbitals and is large enough to increase its coordination number.

A number of oxides and halides of the type AB_2 and AB_3 form such polymeric compounds.

Hydrogen bonding (already discussed) can also be considered as donor-acceptor interaction. In it the acceptor (LUMO) is the unoccupied antibonding orbital of hydrogen bonded to the electronegative element.

3.7   Molecules in Condensed Phases

The solid and liquid phase is known as a **condensed phase**. The condensed phase results due to intermolecular forces. An approximate relationship between the strength of intermolecular forces and the boiling points is provided by **Trouton's Law.** According to it the value of $AS°_{vap}$ is around 90 $JK^{-1}mol^{-1}$ where

$$\Delta S°_{vap} = \frac{\Delta H_{vap}}{T_b}$$

This law is not applicable when molecules have an unusual degree of organization in either the liquid or vapour phase (i.e. due to H–bonding)

Inter Molecular Forces

Various types of intermolecular forces include electrostatic forces, hydrogen bonding, dipole-dipole interactions, London dispersion forces etc. All these have same effects as the boiling points of the substances. In moving down a group the *bp* increase in case of non-polar molecules (*e.g.* $CH_4 < SiH_4 < GeH_4$ etc.). Also $CF_4 < CCl_4 < CBr_4 < CI_4$ etc.

In ionic halides the order is reversed.

Hydrogen bonding also has an effect on the structure of liquids and solids thus ice has a structure in which each water molecule is hydrogen bonded to four hydrogen atoms.

Molecular Polarity

The **polarity** of a molecule is measure in Dehye CD).
$1D = 3.336 \times 10^{-30}$ c.m.

Polarity is a measure of charge dispersion in bonds.

The polarity of a molecule is measured by its dipole moment (μ).

$\mu = q.d.$

Larger dipoles lead to stronger intermolecular forces. The species having dipole moment very nearly equal to the one predicted for ionic compounds do not condense to form molecular solids or liquids.

Dipole moments contribute to **dielectric constants** of liquids or solids. In non-polar substances dielectric constant arises due to *molecular polarizability* and is generally much smaller than with polar molecules.

4

Structure and Bonding in Solids

4.1 Introduction to Solids

Solids. Those substances, which have definite shape and definite volume, are called solids *e.g.* wood, stone.

Types of Solids

(i) **Crystalline solids.** Those solids which are bound by well defined plane faces, have some geometry irrespective of the source from which they are obtained *e.g.* crystals of NaCl.

(ii) **Amorphous solids.** These are super cooled liquids in which the forces of attraction holding the molecules together is so great that the material is rigid, but there is no regularity in structure *e.g.* glass.

Important Terms

Crystallography. It is the study of geometry and symmetry of crystal.

Geometrical crystallography. It is concerned with the description and determination of internal geometry of the crystal.

Crystallites. This refers to the crystalline parts of the amorphous solids.

Space lattice or crystal lattice. The regular pattern of points which describe the three dimensional arrangement of particles (atoms, molecules, ions) in a crystal structure is called **space lattice** or **crystal lattice.**

Structure Types

Rock Salt Structure–NaCl like structure.

Rutile Structure–T_iO_2 like structure.

T_iO_2 is known also as *brookite* and *anatase* in which the arrangement of atoms is different from that in rutile.

Unit Cell

Unit Cell. The smallest portion of the space lattice which can generate the complete crystal by repeating its own dimensions in various directions is called the unit cell of the crystal.

Types of Unit Cells

(i)   *Simple cubic lattice.* In it each corner of a cube is occupied by lattice points.

(ii) *Face centred cubic lattice.* It has eight atoms at its corners and further six atoms are arranged at the centre of each face.

(iii) *Body centred cubic cell.* In it each corner is occupied by lattice points and one lattice point occupies the centre of the unit cell.

The three types of cubic unit cells are illustrated in Fig. 4.1.

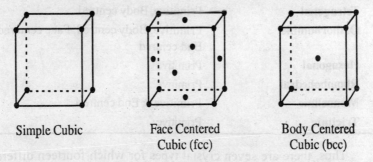

Simple Cubic   Face Centered   Body Centered
                      Cubic (fcc)   Cubic (bcc)

Fig. 4.1. Types of cubic unit cells.

It may be mentioned here that another type of unit cell, called end centred unit cell, is possible for orthorhombic and monoclinic crystal types.

*In an **end centred unit cell**, there are lattice points in the face centres of only one set of faces, in addition to the lattice points at the corners of the unit cell.*

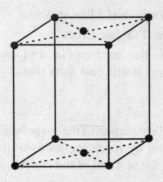

Fig. 4.2. An end centered unit cell.

It may be noted that all the four types of unit cells are not possible for each crystal class.

The various types of unit cells possible for different crystal classes are given below in tabular form:

Crystal class	Possible types of unit cells
Cubic	Primitive, Body centred, Face centered
Tetragonal	Primitive, Body centred
Orthorhombic	Primitive, Body centred, Face centered, End centred
Hexagonal	Primitive
Rhombohedral	Primitive
Monoclinic	Primitive & End centred
Triclinic	Primitive

Thus, there are seven crystal types for which fourteen different types of lattices (7 primitive, 3 body centred, 2 face centered and 2 end centred) are possible. These fourteen different types of lattices are known as **Bravais lattices.**

Lattice points. These are the points which indicates the position of atoms, ions or molecules in a crystal. These are equivalent points and are arranged in some regular pattern in three-dimensional space lattice. Each one of these lattice points have the same environment.

Coordination number. It is the number of atoms or spheres that surround a single atom or sphere in a crystal. The coordination number (C.N.) of both hcp and cubic close packing (ccp) structure is 12. In bcc coordination number is 8 and in fcc the coordination number is 6.

Non-stoichiometry: Most of the pure molecular substances have a definite stoichiometry (*i.e.* the relative number of different types of atom) but it may not be always true for solids.

Calculation of Number of Particles in a Unit Cell

In order to calculate the number of particles in a unit cell, the following rules must be obeyed:

1. Each particle at the corner of a unit cell is shared by eight unit cells in the lattice and hence contributes only $\frac{1}{8}$ to a particular unit cell.

2. A particle at the edge centre is shared by four unit cells in the lattice and hence contributes only $\frac{1}{4}$ to a particular unit cell.

3. A particle at the centre of the face of a unit is shared by two unit cells in the lattice and contributes only $\frac{1}{2}$ to a particular unit cell.

4. A particle at the body centre of a unit cell belongs to the particular unit cell.

Now, by applying these rules, let us calculate the number of atoms in the different cubic unit cells of monoatomic substances.

Simple cubic. In this type of unit cell, there are eight atoms at the corners (Fig. 4.2) and each such atom makes $\frac{1}{8}$ contribution to the unit cell. Hence, *a simple cubic unit cells has*

$$8 \ (at \ corners) \times \frac{1}{8} = 1 \ atom.$$

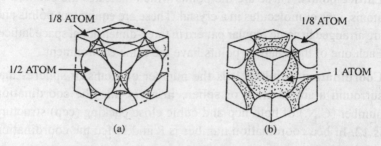

Fig. 4.3. (a) Three-dimensional view showing four atoms per unit cell in case of cubic close-packed structure. (b) Three-dimensional view showing two atoms per unit cell in a body-centred cubic structure.

Body centred cubic. This type of unit cell has eight atoms at corners and one at the body centre. Each corner atom makes $\frac{1}{8}$ contribution and the atom at the body centre belongs only to the particular unit cell. Hence, *a body centred cubic unit cell has*

$$8 \ (at \ corners) \times \frac{1}{8} + 1(at \ body \ centre) \times 1 = 2 \ atoms.$$

Face centred cubic. A face centred cubic unit cell has one atom at each corner (there are eight corners of a cube) and one atom at each face centre (there are six faces of a cube). An atom at the face centre is being shared by two unit cells and makes a contribution of only $\frac{1}{2}$ to a particular unit cell. Hence, *a face centred cubic unit cell has*

$$8 \ (at \ corners) \times \frac{1}{8} + 6(at \ body \ centres) \times \frac{1}{2} = 4 \ atoms.$$

Packing of Constituents in Crystals

In the formation of crystals the constituent particles try to pack as closely as possible so as to attain a state of maximum possible density and stability. Since in different crystals, the units of pattern have different shapes and sizes, the actual mode of closest packing is different for different crystals. In this section, we shall focus on close packing modes of spherical particles of equal size. In metallic crystals the constituent particles are nearly of this type.

Close Packing in Two Dimensions

In order to understand the close packing of spheres, first of all, let us consider how the spheres can be arranged in a plane. The two possible arrangements are shown in Fig. 4.4. in the arrangement *(a)* the spheres in the adjacent rows lie just one over the other and show a horizontal as well as vertical alignment, and form squares. This type of packing is called **square close packing.** Each sphere in this arrangement is in contact with four other spheres.

In the arrangement *(b),* the spheres in every second row are seated in the depressions between the spheres of the first row. The spheres in the third row are vertically aligned with the spheres in the first row and those in fourth row vertically aligned with spheres in the second row. The similar pattern is followed throughout. In this arrangement, each sphere is in direct contact with six other spheres. This arrangement gives rise to hexagonal patterns and is called **hexagonal close packing**.

(a) Square close packing.

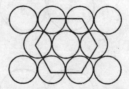

(a) Hexagonal close packing.

Fig. 4.4. (a) Square close packing. (b) Hexagonal close packing.

The arrangement (b) is obviously more closely packed than the arrangement (a). it can be shown by simple calculations that in the arrangement (b) 60.4 per cent of the available space is occupied by spheres whereas in arrangement (a) only 52.4 per cent of the space is occupied by spheres. If only one layer of spheres is to be packed, the spheres will arrange themselves according to hexagonal close packing because it is more efficient. In this arrangement there are a number of vacant spaces or voids. These vacant spaces are between three touching sphere whose centres lie at the corners of an equilateral triangle. These vacant spaces are, therefore, called **triangular voids**.

Close Packing in Three Dimensions

In order to develop three-dimensional close packing, let us retain the hexagonal close packing in the first layer because it is the most efficient. If the spheres in the second layer are just placed over the spheres in the first layer so that the spheres in the two layers are vertically aligned then the voids in the two layers will also cover each other. This will amount to an inefficient filling of space. For close packing each sphere in the second layer rests in the hollow at the centre of three touching spheres in the layer as shown in Fig. 4.5 *(b)*.

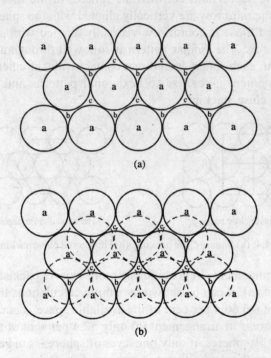

Fig. 4.5. Close packing of spheres.

The spheres in the first layer are shown by solid lines while those in second layer are shown by broken lines. It may be noted that only half the triangular voids in the first layer are occupied by spheres in the second layer (*i.e.* either *b* or *c*). The unoccupied hollows or voids in the first layer are indicated by (c) in Fig. 4.5.

There are two alternative ways in which spheres in the third layer can be arranged over the second layer. The third layer can lie vertically above the first if the spheres in the third layer rest in one set of hollows [corresponding to centres of the spheres (marked by *a*) in the first layer] on the top of the second layer, alternatively, the third layer can be different from the first if the spheres in the third layer lie on the other set of hollows which correspond to those marked '*c*' in the first layer. The first arrangement is called ABAB... type while the second alternative is called ABC ABC... type. These two arrangements are equally efficient. In either type of close packing 74.0 per cent of the available space is occupied by spheres. They differ from each other in overall symmetry. *The AB AB... arrangement has hexagonal symmetry and is known as* **hexagonal close packing (hcp)** (Fig. 4.6). *The ABC ABC... packing has cubic symmetry and is known as* **cubic close packing (ccp)** (Fig. 4.7). The cubic close packing has *face centred cubic* (fcc) unit cell.

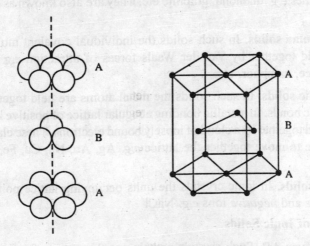

Fig. 4.6. Hexagonal close packing (hcp).

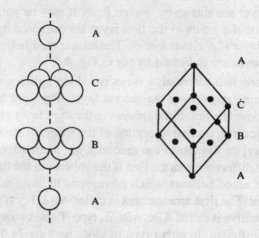

Fig. 4.7. Cubic close packing (ccp).

Chemical Classification of Solids

Covalent or Polymeric solids. In such solids covalent bonds extend throughout the solid and so they may be considered as very large molecules *e.g.* diamond, graphite etc. They are also known as *atomic solids*.

Molecular solids. In such solids the individual covalent molecules are held together by Van der Waals forces of attraction *e.g.* sugar, urea, ice, camphor, etc.

Metallic solids. In such solids the metal atoms are held together by metallic bonds. In metallic bonding a regular lattice of positive kernels are held together by a cloud of loosely bound electrons. These electrons are free to move together the lattice *e.g.* Ag, Au, Na, Cu, Fe, K, Al etc.

Ionic solids. In ionic crystals the units occupying lattice points are *positive* and *negative* ions *e.g.* NaCl

Types of Ionic Solids

(i)   Type **AB.** Such crystals contain equal number of cations and anions *e.g.* NaCl, CsCl, ZnS etc.

(ii) Type **AB$_2$**. In such crystals the number of anions is twice the number of cations *e.g.* CaF$_2$, TiO$_2$ etc.

(iii) Type **AB$_3$**. In such crystals the number of anions is three times the number of cations *e.g.* AlF$_3$.

(iv) **Layer structures.**

Although broad classification is useful but many solids show a degree of intermediate character or even several types of bonding simultaneously.

Metallic Elements

Metallic elements have one of the three structures i.e. ccp, hcp, or bcc. The commonest stable structures observed are

Group 1 elements – bcc

Group 2 elements – varied

Group 3and 4 elements – hcp

Group 5 and 6 elements – bcc

Group 7 and 8 elements – hcp

Group 9 and 11 elements – fcc

In transition metal groups 7, 8 and 9 a number of irregularities have been observed.

The elements Mn, Fe, Co (3rd-series) are exceptions.

Non-Metallic Elements

Boron has an exceptional structure.

In other cases we find the following:

Group 14 — diamond structure (four tetrahedral bands)

Group 15 — Pyramidal (three bands) non-planar.

Group 16 — Non-linear (two bands)

Group 17 — one band

Group 18 — no band (held by vander Waals forces), fcc.

The structural distinction between near neighbours (banded) atoms and the next near neighbour (non-banded) ones becomes less marked down each group. Table below lists the ratio of these distances for some non-metallic elements of periods 3, 4, 5 and shows how the two distances become more nearly equal for heavier elements.

Table

P	1.787	S	1.81	Cl	1.65
As	1.33	Se	1.49	Br	1.46
Sb	1.16	Tc	1.21	I	1.33

4.2 Binary Compounds

Some Simple Structures

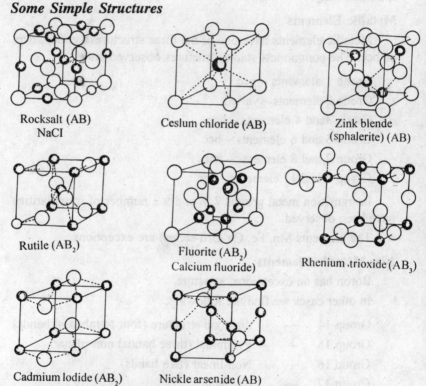

Rocksalt (AB)
NaCl

Cesium chloride (AB)

Zink blende
(sphalerite) (AB)

Rutile (AB$_2$)

Fluorite (AB$_2$)
Calcium fluoride)

Rhenium trioxide (AB$_3$)

Cadmium Iodide (AB$_2$)

Nickle arsenide (AB)

Fig. 4.8. A selection of binary structures.

In the structures shown many of the atoms have a regular coordination geometry:

CN = 2: linear (B in ReO$_3$);

CN = 3: planar (B in rutile);

CN = 4: tetrahedral (A and B in zinc blende, B in fluorite);

CN = 6: octahedral (A and B in rocksalt, A in NiAs, rutile and CdI_2);

CN = 8: cubic (A and B in CsCl, A in fluorite).

These geometries are expected in ionic compounds, as they lead to the greatest spacing between ions with the same charge. Other geometries are sometimes found, however, especially for the nonmetal B atom:

CN = 2: bent (SiO_2 structures, not shown);

CN = 3: pyramidal (in CdI_2);

CN = 6: trigonal prismatic (in NiAs).

The explanation of these must involve nonionic factors.

4.3 Close Packing

A number of binary structures can be obtained from close-packed arrays of atoms of one kind. *Figure 4.9* shows that between adjacent close-packed layers are **octahedral** and **tetrahedral holes** (labelled O and T) such that atoms of another kind occupying these sites would be octahedrally or tetrahedrally coordinated. For ionic compounds we can imagine the larger ions (usually the anions) forming the close-packed array, and cations occupying some of the holes. In either hexagonal (hcp) or cubic close-packed (ccp or fcc) arrays of B there is **one octahedral** and **two tetrahedral holes** per B atom. *Table 4.1* shows some binary structures classified in this way. Thus filling all the octahedral holes in a fcc array generates the **rocksalt** structure (in which the original B atoms are also octahedrally coordinated); doing the same in an hcp array gives the NiAs structure. Filling all the tetrahedral holes in an *fcc* anion array gives the antifluorite structure, more commonly found with anions and cations reserved as in fluorite (CaF_2) itself. A similar arrangement is never found in an hcp array. The tetrahedral holes occur in pairs that are very close together.

When only a fraction of the holes of a given type are occupied there are several possibilities. The most symmetrical way of filling half the tetrahedral holes gives the **zinc blende** structure with ccp, and the very similar 4:4 **wurtzite** (ZnO) structure with hcp. Both the

rutile and **CdI$_2$** structures can be derived by filling half the octahedral holes in hcp. The former gives a more regular coordination of the anions (see above) although the resulting structure is no longer hexagonal. The CdI$_2$ structure arises from alternatively occupying every octahedral hole between two adjacent close-packed planes, and leaving the next layer of holes empty. It is an example of a layer structure based on BAB 'sandwiches' that are stacked with only B-B contacts between them. The CdCl$_2$ structure is based in a similar way on ccp (rather than hcp) anions, and many other layer structures with formulae such as AB$_3$ can be formed by only partial filling of the holes between two layers.

Fig. 4.9. Octahedral (O) and tetrahedral (T) holes between adjacent close-packed layers.

Table 4.1. Some binary structures based on close-packed arrays of anions

Array	Holes filled	Structure type	Examples
Fcc	All octahedral	Rocksalt (NaCl)	LiF, MgO
	½ octahedral	Cadmium chloride (CdCl$_2$)[a]	MgCl$_2$
	All tetrahedral	Antifluorite	Li$_2$O
	½ tetrahedral	Sphalerite (zinc blende)	ZnS, CuCl
	½ tetrahedral	Lead oxide (PbO)[a]	SnO
Hcp	All octahedral	Nickel arsenide (NiAs)	FeS

Array	Holes filled	Structure type	Examples
	½ octahedral	Rutile[b]	MgF_2, TiO_2
	½ octahedral	Cadmium iodide (CdI_2)	TiS_2
	All tetrahedral	*Not found*	—
	½ tetrahedral	Wurtzite	BeO, ZnO

[a] Layer structures.

[b] Filling the holes changes the symmetry; the rutile unit cell is not hexagonal.

4.4 Linked Polyhedra

Another way of analyzing binary structures is to concentrate on the coordination polyhedra is one type of atom, and on the way these are linked together. This approach is generally useful in structures with covalent bonding, and/or ones that are more open than those derived from close packing.

If two tetrahedral AB_4 units share one B atom in common (1) we talk of corner **sharing.** A corner-shared pair has stoichiometry A_2B_7 and is found in (molecular) Cl_2O_7 and occasionally in silicates. Tetrahedral each sharing corners with two others generate a chain or ring LO (2) of stoichiometry AB_3 is found with SO_3 commonly in silicates (see Topics D5 and G4). These structures are often represented by drawing the tetrahedral without showing the atoms explicitly. Rings and chains with two corners shared are shown in this way (*Fig. 4.10a* and *b*). Sharing three corners makes a layer or a tetrahedral cluster of stoichiometry A_2O_3 such layers occur in silicates, and the clusters as P_4O_{10} molecules. Tetrahedra sharing all four corners with others generate a 3D **framework** of stoichiometry AB_2, found in the various (crystalline and glassy) structures of SiO_2.

1

2

Tetrahedra with two B atoms in common are said to be edge sharing: examples of isolated edge-sharing pairs are B_2H_6 and Al_2Cl_6. A chain of Tetrahedra each sharing two edges with other has a stoichiometry AB_2 and is found as the **chain structures** of BeH_2 and SiS_2, shown in *Fig. 4.10(c)*. Face sharing is also possible but is almost never found with the tetrahedra as the A atoms would be very close together.

Similar ideas can be used with octahedra. Chains of corner sharing octahedra are found in $WOBr_4$ and of edge-sharing octahedra in NbI_4. If octahedra share all six corners, the 3D ReO_3 structure results (see *Fig. 4.10d*).

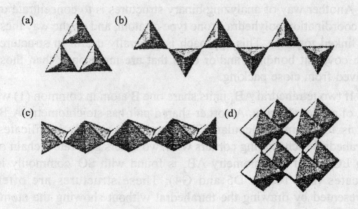

Fig. 4.10. Structures derived from linking of polyhedra (see text).

Factors Influencing Structure

Ionic Radii

The following trends have been observed

(i)   For isoelectronic ions, radii decreases with increasing positive charge.

(ii) As we move down a group ionic radii increases.

(iii) For elements of variable oxidation states radii decreases with increasing positive charge.

(iv) Anions are longer than cations.

(v) Ionic radii increase with coordination number.

Radius Ratio

It is the ratio of cations to that of anion present.

$$\text{Radius ratio} = \frac{r_+}{r_-}$$

The approximate radius ratio for different coordination numbers are given below.

Limiting Radii Ratio, $\dfrac{r}{R}$	Coordination Number	Shape
0.155—0.225	3	Plane trigonal
0.255—0.414	4	Tetrahedral
0.414—0.732	4	Square planar
0.414—0.732	4	Octahedral
0.732—1.00	8	Body centred cubic (bcc)

Ionic Polarizability

Polarizability of an atom is the ability of the applied electric field to distort the electric cloud and thus induce an electric dipole moment.

The most polarisable ions are larger ones (e.g. S^{2-}, B_r^-, I^- etc).

Polarisation lowers the energy of **anions** in layer and chain structures because generally in these the anions are in asymmetric environment and they experience a strong net electric field from neighbouring ions. In such a situation polarization stabilizes an ion. This is not possible in compounds with coordination symmetry. The occurrence in layer structure of disulphide and dichloride may be attributed to stabilization effect. The stabilization is not possible in oxides and fluorides (smaller anions).

TiO_2 and FeF_2 both have **rutile** structure.

TiS_2 and FeI_2 both have **CdI_2** structure.

Cr_2O is a rare example of the anti CdI_2 structure with adjacent layers of Cs^+, the high polarijability of Cs^+ ion must be a contributing factor.

Covalent Bonding

Covalent bonds have directional character. Such bonds are generally formed by non-metallic elements. In such compounds the structures can be rationalized by coordination number and bonding geometry of atoms present e.g.,

In SiC, both elements have tetrahedral coordination.

In SiO_2, Si may form four tetrahedral bonds and oxygen bonds with a non-linear geometry.

The structural effects shown by compounds of some less electro positive elements may be attributed to partial covalent bonding in them e.g., CuCl and ZnO have structures of tetrahedral coordination, though on the basis of their radii the (octahedral) **rocksalt** like structure is more probable.

Mercury is an example of lower coordination numbers, generally found with post transition metals. Hg^{2+} compounds have low ionic character, and two coordination is quite common.

Covalent bonding interaction can take place between similar atoms.

4.5 More Complex Solids

Bonding between atoms of the same kind is generally present in those binary compounds which show anomalous stoichiometry e.g. NaO, KO_2, LiS, CaC_2, NaN_3. They contain O_2^{2-}, O_2^-, S_2^{2-}, C_2^{2-}, N_3^- ions respectively.

Zinti compounds are the compounds formed by the combination of an electropositive metal with a *p*-block element of intermediate electronegativity. Some of such compounds contain discrete polymeric units such as Ge_4 tetrahedral in KGe. In some others we find continuous bonded networks such as Si chains in CaSi, or layers as in $CaSi_2$.

The term **metal-metal bonding** is used when homoelement bonding involves the more electropositive element of a binary pair e.g., HgCl contains homo nuclear Hg_2Cl_2 units with Hg-Hg bonds. In GaS also we find Ga-Ga bonds.

Metal rich compounds are formed by early transition metals e.g., Sc_2Cl_3 and $ZnCl_4$. in them we find extensive metal-metal bonding. Such compounds are common with 4d- and 5d-series e.g. $MoCl_2$ which contains clusters of $|Mo_6Cl_6|^{4+}$ with a metal-metal bonded Mo octahedron. Metal-metal bonding sometimes give rise to anomalous magnetic and other properties.

Ternary structure. Such structures are ones with three elements present (e.g $CaCO_3$, $CaTiO_3$). The two possible fundamentally different features of such compounds are

(i) **Complex oxides.** e.g. $CaCO_3$ whose structure is based on rock-salt with the different sites occupied by Ca^{2+} and Co_3^{2-} ions.

(ii) **Mixed oxides** e.g. $CaTiO_3$. It does not have discrete titanate ions. The **perovskite** structure (Fig 4.11) shows a corner sharing network of TiO_6 tetrahedra (essentially the ReO_2 structure) with Ca^{2+} occupying the large central site coordinated by 12 oxygen atoms.

The above division is not absolute and the examples of intermediate structures are found in many a silicates.

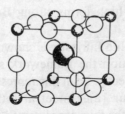

Fig. 4.11. Unit cell of the perovskite structure of $CaTiO_3$.

$ZrSiO_4$ (Zircon) contains discrete SiO_4^{-4} ions.

$CaSiO_3$ does not contain SiO_3^{2-} units but is formed from tetrahedral SiO_4 groups sharing corners to make rings or infinite chains.

Complex oxides are normally found when a nonmetal is present, with oxoanions such as nitrate NO_3^- carbonate CO_3^{2-}, phosphate PO_4^{3-} or sulfate SO_4^{2-}, but are also sometimes formed by metals in high oxidation states (e.g. permanganate MnO_4^- in $KMnO_4$). When a compound contains two metallic elements the mixed oxide form is more normal, but it is important to note that the compound formula itself provides very little guide to the structure (compare $CaCO_3$ and $CaSiO_3$ above). A similar structural variety is found with complex halides. For example, the K_2NiF_4 structure is based on layers of corner-sharing NiF_6 octahedra with no discrete complex ions, whereas K_2PtCl_4 contains individual square planar ions $[PtCl_4]^{2-}$. These differences reflect the bonding preferences of Ni^{II} and Pt^{II}.

Microporous Solids

Zeolites are aluminosillicate solids based on a framework of corner-sharing SiO_4 and AlO_4 tetrahedra. These frameworks contain pores and channels of molecular dimensions, which in natural minerals (or after laboratory synthesis) contain species such as water and hydrated ions. Removal of these species (e.g. by careful heating under vacuum) leads to microporous materials with empty channels and pores. It is possible to make synthetic zeolites of composition SiO_2 with no aluminum, but when Al^{III} is present the framework formula is $[Al_tSi_{t-1}O_2]^{t-}$ and the charge must be compensated by extra-framework cations. In as-prepared zeolites these may be alkali cations, NH_4^* or organic amines, but when the pore materials are removed they are replaced by H^*, which forms strong **Brensted acid** sites within the pores.

The structure of the zeolite **faujasite** is shown in *Figure 4.11*. In this convention representation the framework structure is shown without depicting, atoms directly. Each line represents an Si–O–Si or Si–O–Al connection. Four lines meet at tetrahedral vertices representing the positions of the four-coordinate Si or Al atoms. Space-filling models of this zeolite show that the pores can accommodate molecules up to about 750 pm in diameter.

In their hydrated forms zeolites are used for ion exchange purposes, for example, water softening by replacement of Ca^{2-} with Na^+ or another ion. When dehydrated they have important catalytic applications, promoted by the Brensted acid sites, and by the large area of 'internal surface'. They are used for the cracking of petroleum and for the isomerization of hydrocarbons, where limited pore size exerts a 'shape selectivity', which allows one desirable product to be formed in high yield.

Intercalation and Insertion Compounds

Alkali metals and bromine react with graphite to form solids known as **intercalation compounds**, where the foreign atoms are inserted between the intact graphite layers. Many other layered solids, for example dichalcogenides such as TaS_2, which have structures similar to CdI_2 will also for intercalation compounds. The inserted species may be alkali metals, or electron donor molecules such as amines or organometallic compounds. Sometimes compounds of definite composition may be formed, such as KC_6 or C_8Br, but in other cases intercalated phases may be nonstoichiometric such as Li_2TiS_2 ($O < x < 1$). Most interaction reactions involve electron transfer between the guest and the host, and modify the electronic properties.

The term insertion compound is used for solids where atoms or ions enter a three-dimensional framework without disrupting its essential structure. Many **oxide bronzes** are of this type, based on transition metal oxides with inserted alkali or other electropositive metals. For example, the **sodium tungsten bronzes** are of composition Na_xWO_3 where x can range from zero up to 0.9. Their structures are based on the ReO_3 framework with Na occupying the large vacant site. The structure therefore resembles that of perovksite (*Fig. 4.11*) except that the site occupied by Ca in $CaTiO_3$ is only partially occupied in Na_xWO_3 As with intercalation, electron transfer is also involved, and Na_xWO_3 has a metallic appearance and good electronic conductivity whereas pure WO_3 is a pale yellow insulator.

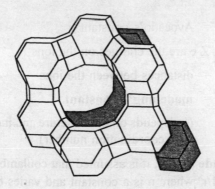

Fig. 4.12. Representation of the structure of the faujasite (see text).

4.6 Lattice Energy

Lattice energy of an ionic compound is the energy required to separate the solid into gas phase ions.

The Born-haber cycle: It is used to estimate the lattice energy of ionic solids. It makes use of Hess's law

$$H_L(NaCl) = -\Delta H_f(NaCl) + \Delta H_{at}(Na) + \tfrac{1}{2}B(Cl_2) + l(Na) - A(Cl)$$

l(Na) is greater than A (Cl) in the above equation. This shows that Na and Cl atoms are more stable than the ion Na^+ and Cl^- and it is the lattice energy that stabilizes the ionic charge distribution in solid NaCl.

$$Na(g) + cl(g) \xrightarrow{l(Na) - A(cl)} Na^+(g) + cl^-(g)$$

$$\Delta H_{at}(Na) + \tfrac{1}{2}B(cl-cl) \uparrow \qquad \qquad \uparrow H_2(Nacl)$$

$$Na(g) + \tfrac{1}{2}cl_2(g) \xrightarrow[\Delta H_f(Nacl)]{} Nacl(s)$$

Theoretical Estimates

$$u_c = \frac{N_o . AZ_+Z_-e^2}{4\pi \in_o r_o} \quad \text{(In coloumbic interaction model)}$$

where N_0 = Avocado's constant

Z_+e, Z_-e are the charges on the ions

r_0 = distances between the ions

A = **madelung's constant**

(It depends on the structure and increases slowly with coordination number)

In **Born-Iande Model,** it is assumed that coulambic repulsion is proportional to $1/r^n$ where n is a constant and varies between 7 and 12. In this case we get

$$U_L = \frac{N_o \cdot A Z_+ Z_- e^2}{4\pi \epsilon_o r_o}\left(1 - \frac{1}{n}\right)$$

It is called **Born-Mayer equation.**

Kapustinskii Equation

In this the **Madelung constant (A)** and **repulsive parameter (n)** are put equal to average values and the interionic distance is assumed to be equal to $(r_+ + r_-)$. This equation then becomes

$$u_c = \frac{C \cdot V \cdot z_+ z_-}{(r_+ + r_-)}$$

where r is the number of ions in formula units

This is more useful because it emphasizes two essential features of lattice energy even if the bonding is not fully ionic.

(i) Lattice energy increases with increasing charge on the ions.

(ii) Lattice energies are always larger for smaller ions.

Applications: This equation is used rationalize many observation in inorganic chemistry. E.g.

(i) **Group oxidation states:** the occurrence of Nz^+, Mg^{2+}, Al^{3+} etc., depends on the balance between the energies required to form them in the gas phase and the lattice energies that stabilize them in solids (already discussed for NaCl).

The lattice energy of $Mg\,F_2$ is much larger than that of Mg F. However, the enthalpy of formation of MgF_2 is much more negative and so Mg F(s) is unknown because it spontaneously disproportionates.

$$2\,Mg\,F(s) \longrightarrow Mg(s) + Mg\,F_2\,(s)$$

(ii) **Stabilization of High and Low Oxidation States:** Small and/ or highly charged ions provide highest lattice energies and the increase in lattice energy with higher oxidation state is more likely to compensate for high IE.

A large ion with low charge is more likely to stabilize a low oxidation state (e.g. I^-)

CuF is not known but other halides of Cu are known. It may be due to increase in lattice energy from CuF to CuF_2 is sufficient to force a disproportion reaction like that of Mg F. However, CuX_2 is stable with X = F, Cl, Br but not I.

(iii) Stabilization of large anions or cations: Generally a **large cation stabilizes a large anion.**

4.5 Electrical and Optical Properties of Solids

1. Electrical Properties

On the basis of electrical conductivity the solids can be broadly classified into three types:

(a) Metals (conductors)

(b) Insulators

(c) Semi-conductors.

Electrical conductivity of metals is very high and is of the order of $10^6 - 10^8$ ohm^{-1} cm^{-1} while that of insulators is of the order of 10^{-12} ohm^{-1} cm^{-1}. Semi-conductors have intermediate conductivity which lies in the range $10^2 - 10^{-9}$ ohm^{-1} cm^{-1}. Electrical conductivity of solids may arise through the motion of electrons and positive holes (electronic conductivity) or through the motion of ions (ionic conductivity). The conduction through electrons is called *n-type conduction* and through positive holes is called *p-type conduction.* Pure ionic solids where conduction can take place only through motion of ions are insulators. However, the presence of defects in the crystal structure increases their conductivity.

Unlike metals, the conductivity of semi-conductors and insulators is mainly due to the presence of interstitial electrons and positive holes in the solids due to imperfections. *The conductivity of semiconductors and insulators increases with increase in temperature while that of metals decreases.*

The electrical behaviour of some oxides of transition metals (belonging to fourth period) is given in Table 4.2. It may be noted that these oxides show wide variation in their electrical behaviour.

Table 4.2. Electrical Properties of Some Transition Oxides

TiO(M)	VO(M)		MnO(I)	FeO(I)	CoO(I) NiO(I) CuO(I)
Ti_2O_3(M–1)	V_2O_3(M)(I)	Cr_2O_3(I)	Mn_2O_3(I)	Fe_2O_3(I)	
TiO_2(I)	VO_2(M–I)	CrO_2(M)	MnO_2(I)		
	V_2O_5(I)				

M = Metal; I = Insulator; M – I = shows a transition from metal to insulator behaviour at a certain temperature.

2. Magnetic Properties

Solids can be classified into different types depending upon their behaviour towards magnetic fields. *The substances which are weakly repelled by magnetic field* are called **diamagnetic substances.** For example, TiO_2 and NaCl. Diamagnetic substances have all their electrons paired.

The substances which are weakly attracted by magnetic field are called **paramagnetic substances**. These substances have permanent magnetic dipoles due to the presence of some species (atoms, ions or molecules) with unpaired electrons. The paramagnetic substances lose their magnetism in the absence of magnetic field. For example, TiO, VO_2 and CuO.

The substances which are strongly attracted by magnetic field are called **ferromagnetic substances.** These substances show permanent magnetism even in the absence of magnetic field. Some examples of ferromagnetic solids are : iron, cobalt, nickel and CrO_2 .

Ferromagnetism arises due to spontaneous alignment of magnetic moments of ions or atoms in the same direction [Fig. 4.13(a)]. Alignment of magnetic moments in opposite direction in a compensatory manner and resulting in a zero magnetic moment (due to equal number of parallel and antiparallel magnetic dipoles) gives rise to *antiferromagnetism* [Fig. *4.13(b)*]. For example, MnO, Mn_2O_3 and MnO_2 are antiferromagnetic. Alignment of magnetic moments in opposite directions resulting in a net magnetic moment (due to unequal number of parallel and antiparallel magnetic dipoles) gives rise to *ferrimagnetism* [Fig. *4.13(c)*]. For example, Fe_3O_4 is ferrimagnetic.

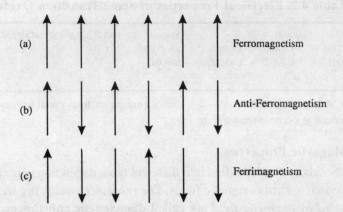

Fig. 4.13. Alignment of magnetic dipoles in (a) Ferromagnetic, (b) Antiferro-magnetic and (c) ferrimagnetic substances.

Ferromagnetic and ferrimagnetic substances change into paramagnetic substances at higher temperatures due to randomization of spins. Fe_3O_4, which is ferrimagnetic at room temperature, becomes paramagnetic at 850 K.

Magnetic behaviour of some oxides of transition metals are given in Table 4.3.

Table 4.3. Magnetic Properties of Some Transition Metal Oxides

TiO(p)	VO(p)		MnO(af)	FeO(af)	CoO(af)NiO(af) CuO(p)
Ti_2O_3(p)	V_2O_3(af)	Cr_2O_3(af)	Mn_2O_3(af)	Fe_2O_3(af)	
TiO_2(d)	VO_2(p)	CrO_2(f)	MnO_2(af)	Fe_3O_4(fe)	
	V_2O_5(d)				

P = paramagnetic; af = anti-feromagnetic; fe = ferrimagnetic; f = ferromagnetic; d = diamagnetic.

3. Dielectric Properties

A **dielectric** is *a substance in which an electric field gives rise to no net flow of electric charge.* This is due to the reason that electrons in a electric are tightly held by individual atoms. However, under the effect of applied field displacement of charges takes place, resulting in the creation of dipoles.

The alignment of these dipoles in different ways, *i.e.,* compensatory way (zero dipole) or non-compensatory way (net dipole) impart certain characteristics properties to solids.

The dipoles may align in such a way so that there is net dipole moment in the crystals. Crystals of this type exhibit **piezoelectricity** or **piezoelectric effect,** *i.e.,* when such crystals are subjected to a pressure or mechanical stress, electricity is produced. Conversely, if an electric field is applied to such a crystal, the crystal gets deformed due to generation of mechanical strain. This is sometimes called **inverse piezoelectric effect.** The piezoelectric crystals are used as pickups in record players, where they produce electrical signals by application of pressure.

Certain crystals when heated, acquire electric charges on opposite faces. This property of the crystal is known as **pyroelectricity.**

There are certain crystals in which dipoles are spontaneously aligned in a particular direction, even in the absence of electric field. Such substances are called **ferroelectric substances** and the phenomenon is called **ferroelectricty.** The direction of polarization in these substances can be changed by applying electric field. Baruion titanate ($BaTiO_3$), sodium potassium tartarate (*Rochelle salt*), and potassium hydrozen phosphate (KH_2IO_4) are ferroelectric solids. If the alternate dipoles are in opposite directions, then the net dipole moment will be zero and the crystal is called **antiferroelectric.** Lead zirconate ($PbZrO_3$) is an antiferroelectric solid.

4.8   Crystal Defects in Solids

Ideal crystal. An ideal crystal is one which has the same unit cell containing the same lattice points across the whole of the crystal.

Crystal defect. A defect generally denotes departure from regularity in the arrangement of the constituent particles (atoms, ions or molecules) in a crystal.

Thermodynamic defects. Those defects which depend upon the temperature are called thermodynamic defects.

Point defects. If in a crystal there occurs a defect either due to missing particle or due to dislocation of a constituent particle to a position meant for another particle of shifting to interstitial position, then this is known as point defect.

Lattice imperfections. When the deviation from regular pattern extend over microscopic regions of the crystals, these are called lattice imperfections.

Structural imperfection. A structural defect in a crystal lattice is called structural imperfection.

Chemical imperfection. The imperfections arising due to presence of impurities are known as chemical imperfection.

Extrinsic imperfection. This type of defect arises due to departure from regular chemical composition. It is also known as *chemical defect.*

Electronic imperfection. Electrons in solids are considered as imperfections. The electron deficient bond produce by the removal of electron by heating solids above 0 K, is referred as a *hole.* Holes give rise to electrical conductivity. The concentration of holes and electrons will be equal in pure crystals. Electrons and holes can be preferentially produced in such covalent crystals by adding impurities.

13-15 compounds. When solid state materials are produced by combination of elements of group 13 and group 15, they are called **13-15 compounds** *e.g.* InSb, AIP, GaAs etc.

12-16 compounds. When solid state compounds are obtained by combination of elements of group 12 and group 16, they are called **12-16 compounds** *e.g.* ZnS, CdS, CdSe, HgTe etc.

Line defects or dislocation. When lattice imperfections are along lines these are called *line defects* or *dislocations.*

Plane defects. When lattice imperfections are along surfaces these are called *plane defects.*

Schottky defects. In Schottky defect atom or ion is missing from normal site creating a vacancy. A vacancy of one of the ions is accompanied by the vacancy of the oppositely charged ions so that electrical neutrality is still maintained.

Due to the presence of this defect in a compound (*e.g.* AgBr), the overall density of the compound decreases.

There are about 10^6 schottky pairs per *cc* at room temperature in NaCl. In one *cc* of NaCl there are about 10^{22} ions, so there will be one schottky defect per 10^{16} ions.

Frenkel defect. In Frenkel defect atom or ion in normal site is displaced to an interstitial site thus creating a vacancy. In this defect ion is not completely missing but only shifted to interstitial site from its normal site. This defect is found in AgBr.

Interstitial. In interstitial an atom or ion is found in a normally vacant interstitial site.

Non-stoichiometric defects

(a) **Metal Excess Defect**

    (i) *Metal excess defect.* In this defect positive charge is in excess. It may be due to the fact that a negative ion is missing from its position and the hole so created is occupied by an electron to maintain electrical neutrality.

    When NaCl is treated with sodium vapour, a yellow non-stoichiometric form of NaCl is obtained in which there is excess of Na^+ ions.

    (ii) *Metal excess defect.* In this case an extra positive ion may be present in an interstitial site and to maintain electrical neutrality an electron is also present in an interstitial space. This defect is found in ZnO.

(b) **Metal deficiency defects.** It arises in following ways:

    (i) A positive ion may be missing from its lattice site and the extra negative charge is balanced by an adjacent metal ion having two charges instead of one. This type of defect is shown by FeO, FeS, NiO etc.

    (ii) An extra negative ion may find an interstitial position and the charges are balanced by means of an extra charge on an adjacent metal ion.

F-centre. Electrons trapped in anion vacancies are referred to as F-centres. These centres gives rise to interesting properties. Excess of potassium ion in KCl makes the crystal appear violet and the excess of Li^+ in LiCl makes it appear pink.

Semi-conductors. It refers to those elements whose conductivity increases with the increase in temperature e.g., impurity doped silicon and germanium.

Dielectric constant of a medium is a measure of the electrostatic polarization, which reduces the forces between charges

Static dielectric constant depends on the displacement of ions from their regular positions in an applied electric field.

The **High Frequency dielectric constant** is measured at the frequencies faster than the vibrational motion of ions. It is applicable to the visible region of the spectrum. It determines **refractive index** which governs the transmission of light in transparent media.

Chemistry in Solution

5.1 Solvent Types and Properties

Solvent is a liquid medium in which dissolved substances are known as **solutes**.

Solvents are useful

(i) for storing those substances which otherwise would be is inconvenient states (*e.g.* gases).

(ii) for facilitating those reactions that would otherwise be hard to carry out (*e.g.* reaction involving solids)

Some substances that are useful solvents are Acetonitrile, ammonia, benzene, BF_3, Dimethyl sulphoxide $(CH_3)_2$ SO (DMSO), HF, C_6H_{14} (n-hexane), propane (acetone), pyridine, sulphurdioxide, sulphuric acid, tetra hydrofuran (THF) and water.

Molecules with large dipole moments (*e.g.* water, ammonia etc.) are called **polar solvents**. In such solvents, solutes undergo strong **salvation**. For example, Born Model predicts that Gibbs free energy of an ion with large q (in coulambs) and radius r will be changed in solvent compared with gas phase by the amount

$$\Delta G_{solv} = -\frac{q^2}{8\pi \in_0 r}\left(1 - \frac{1}{\in_T}\right)$$

It is also possible that neutral molecules may also be solvated.

Solvation produces a decrease in entropy that may be substantial with highly charged ions and contribute to acid-base strength, complex formation, and solubility trends.

Non-polar solvents (*e.g.* u-hexane) have molecules with little or no dipole moment and low dielectric constants. They dissolve non-polar solutes. They are generally poor solvents for polar molecules.

Ionic substances can dissolve in non-polar solvents if the ions are efficiently solvated by approximate donor and acceptor interaction. Liquid ammonia ($\in_T = 22$) is a good solvent for some ionic compounds, ion pairing is much more common than in water ($\in_T = 82$)

Donor and Acceptor Properties

Most of the polar solvents have **donor** (or **Lewis base**) properties. Such solvents (*e.g.* H_2O, NH_3, pyridine etc.) are efficient at solvating cations and other Levis acids.

Acceptor (or **Lewis acid**) behaviour is important for solvating anions.

Donor and **Acceptor numbers** have been defined by measuring the strength of interaction between solvent molecules and 'standard' acceptor ($SbCl_5$) and donor ($POCl_3$) molecules respectively.

Table 5.1

Ion transferred	Solvent system species			Other examples of	
	Solvent	Acid	Base	Acids	Bases
H^+	H_2O	H_3O^+	OH^-	HNO_3	NH_3
	NH_3	NH_4^+	NH_2^-	H_2O	Na_2O
	H_2SO_4	$H_3SO_4^+$	HSO_4^-	HSO_3F	HNO_3
F^-	BrF_3	BrF_2^+	BrF_4^-	SnF_4	KF
O^{2-}	$CaSiO_3$	SiO_2	O^{2-}	P_2O_5	$CaCO_3$

Benzene has no appreciable donor strength yet it dissolves silver per chlorate, $AgClO_4$. It may be due to strong 'soft' donor-acceptor interaction between Ag^+ and a benzene molecule.

In a number of reactions donor-acceptor interaction may just be the first step in a more substantial **solvolysis reactions**: Such reactions are common in non-metal halides and oxides in water *e.g.*

$$POCl_3 + 6H_2O \longrightarrow OP(OH)_3 + 3H_3O^+ + 3Cl^-$$

$$POCl_3 + 6NH_3 \longrightarrow OP(NH_2)_3 + 3NH_4^+ + 3Cl^-$$

In some reactions a number of products are formed depending on the solvent *e.g.*

$$FeCl_3 \longrightarrow [FeCl_3S] \quad \text{in pyridine}$$

$$\longrightarrow [FeCl_2S_4]^+ + Cl^- \quad \text{in DMSO}$$

$$\longrightarrow [FeCl_2S_4]^+ + [FeCl_4]^- \quad \text{in methyl cyanide}$$

where S represents a coordinated solvent molecule.

Ion Transfer Solvents

Autoprotolysis:

$$2\,H_2O \rightleftharpoons H_3O^+ + OH^-$$

$$2\,NH_3 \rightleftharpoons NH_3^+ + NH_2^-$$

This process of protic solvents is called **autoprotolysis.**

On this basis **acid** is a positive species formed by autoprotolysis and **base** is a negative species formed by autoprotolysis.

It is possible that some thing acting as an acid in one solvent may act as base in another.

Aprotic solvents do not have transferable H$^+$ but some other ion as *oxide* or *halide* may be involved *e.g.*

$$\underset{\text{(base)}}{2\,Br\,F_3} + \underset{\text{(acid)}}{Su\,F_4} \longrightarrow 2\,Br\,F_2^+ + Su\,F_6^-$$

In oxide melts, the solvent system corresponds to **Lux-Flood acid-base** definition according to which an *oxide donor* is a **base** and an *oxide acceptor* is an **acid**.

$$\underset{\text{(base)}}{Ca\,O} + \underset{\text{(acid)}}{Si\,O_2} \longrightarrow Ca\,Si\,O_3$$

5.2   Bronsted Acids and Bases

Lowry-Bronsted Definition. While the classical definitions were adequate for some purposes, these did not explain why a given acid does not dissociate to the same extent in all solvents or why methylamine, CH_3NH_2 can be regarded as a base, since there is no OH group present in the molecule at all.

A more satisfactory definition of acids and bases was given by Lowry and Bronsted. According to them *an acid is a substance with a tendency to lose protons and a base is a substance with a tendency to gain protons.* In other words, *acids are proton donors or protogenic* whereas *bases are proton acceptors or protophilic.*

These tendencies are, however, apparent only if the molecules are present. Thus dissociation of an acid in aqueous solution may be regarded as a reaction with water in which the latter accepts a proton and thereby acts as a base. In the case of a strong acid HX this proton transfer is complete.

$$HX \;+\; H_2O \;\longrightarrow\; H_3O^+ \;+\; X^-$$

$$\underset{\text{(Proton donor)}}{\underset{\text{Acid}}{}} \qquad \underset{\textit{Base}}{\underset{\text{Proton acceptor}}{}} \qquad \underset{\text{ion}}{\underset{\text{Hydronium}}{}}$$

If however, HA is a weak acid, an equilibrium is set up in its aqueous solution as given below:

$$HA \;+\; H_2O \;\rightleftharpoons\; H_2O^+ \;+\; A^-$$

Similarly strong bases like NaOH, KOH, etc., dissociate completely when dissolved in water.

Since OH^- ions have high affinity for protons, NaOH is a proton acceptor and hence is a strong base.

Examples of weak bases are ammonia (NH_3 and its alkyl derivatives called amines). An equilibrium is set up in aqueous solutions.

$$RNH_2 \;+\; H_2O \;\rightleftharpoons\; RNH_3^+ \;+\; OH^-$$

$$\underset{(\textit{A base})}{\underset{\text{Proton acceptor}}{}} \qquad \underset{(\textit{Au acid})}{\underset{\text{Proton acceptor}}{}}$$

Conjugated Acid-Base Pair

$$HA + B \longrightarrow A^+ + HB^-$$

HA is called conjugated acid of A^-

A^- is conjugated base to HA.

They differ by H^+.

Bronsted acidity is solvent dependent.

Self-ionization of Water

$$2H_2O \longrightarrow H_3O^+ + OH^-$$

The equilibrium constant is

$$K_w = [H_3O^+][OH^-] = 1.0 \times 10^{-14} \text{ at } 298k$$

The pH scale is defined by

$$pH = -\log [H_3O^+]$$

Neutral water has a pH of seven, acidic solutions have lower values and basic solutions have higher values.

pH scale provides a convenient means of stating the degree of acidity of a solution. *pH* of pure water at 298 K = 7. At 298 K *pH* of acid solution always < 7 whereas that of alkaline solutions is always > 7.

Calculation of concentration of H^+ ions from *pH* or *K* from *pK*.

Since

$$pH = -\log [H^+]$$
$$\text{Log } [H^+] = -pH$$

Before taking the antilogarithm, it is necessary to make the matissa, *i.e.*, the part lying to the right of the decimal point, if any, positive. This is done as follows:

(i) Add one to matissa part lying right and subtract one part from the characteristics. For example, if the *pH* of a solution is 5.4 we will write

$$pH = -\log [H^+] = 5.4$$
$$\text{or} \quad \log [H^+] = -5.4 = -5-1+(1-0.4) = 6.6 \dots\dots (i)$$

(ii) Take the antilogarithm of matissa,

     e.g., antilog $0.6 = 3.981$

(iii) Multiply this by 10 raised to power of characteristics *i.e.,* the number on the left of the decimal point in *(i)*.

Thus concentration of H^+ ions in this solution $= 3.981 \times 10^{-8}$

In alkaline solution $(OH^{-7}) > (H^+)$

Strong and Weak Behaviour

Strength of Acids and Bases. The strength of an acid or a base is measured by its tendency to lose or gain protons. A strong acid is a substance which loses a proton easily.

$$\underset{\substack{\text{Proton donor} \\ \text{(a strong acid)}}}{HCl} + \underset{\substack{\text{Proton acceptor} \\ \text{(a strong base)}}}{H_2O} \longrightarrow \underset{}{H_3O^+} + \underset{\substack{\text{Conjugate base of HCl} \\ \text{(a weak base)}}}{Cl^-}$$

HCl is a proton donor and loses a proton easily. It is, therefore, a stronger acid. H_2O acts as a base and accepts the proton from HCl easily. It is a strong base. Cl^- is a conjugate base of HCl and has little tendency to accept proton. It is, therefore, a weak base.

In general, *conjugate base of a strong acid is a weak base. Conversely conjugate base of a weak acid is a strong base.*

$$\underset{\text{Weak acid}}{HS^-} + H_2O \rightleftharpoons H_2O^+ + \underset{\text{Strong base}}{S^{2-}}$$

In comparison to HS^-, H_3O^+ has a greater tendency to lose a proton, which is readily accepted by S^{2-} ion. HS^- is, therefore, a weak acid and S^{2-} is a strong base. This justifies the above statement that conjugate base of a weak acid is a strong base.

The equilibrium constant, K_a of an acid is a measure of its ability to lose a proton (its acid strength). The larger value of the equilibrium constant (acid dissociation constant).

$$K_a = \frac{[H_3O^+][A^-]}{[HA]}$$

the higher the concentration of H_3O^+ and stronger the acid.

Strength of a base is measured by its tendency to gain protons.

In the reaction of a base with water

$$B + H_2O \rightleftharpoons BH^+ + OH^-$$

the equilibrium constant (or base dissociation constant), K_b of a base is a measure of its ability to gain a proton (its base strength). The larger the value of the equilibrium constant,

$$K_b = \frac{[BH^+][OH^-]}{[B]}$$

the higher the concentration of OH^- and stronger the base.

K_b is called the **basicity constant.**

The corresponding pK_b values can be found from the equilibrium

$$B + H_2O = BH^+ + OH^-$$

For **strong bases** $pK_b < 0$

For **weak bases** $pK_b > 0$

pK_b for $NH_3 = 4.75$, pK_b for $F^- = 10.55$.

A strong acid (*e.g.* HCl) is fully protolysed and it is impossible to study this species in water. (H_3O^+) is effectively the strongest acid possible there and any stronger acid is said to be **levelled**. Similarly a strong base such as NH_2^- is **levelled** to strongest base possible in water OH^-. Thus **solvent levelling** limits the range of acid-base behaviour that can be observed in any given solvent. It is one of the reasons for use of other solvents with different levelling ranges. *E.g.* Liquid ammonia is very basic as compared to water and H_2SO_4 is very acidic.

Trends in pK Values

Entropy change will tend to reduce the acid strength of any species giving a conjugate base with strongly localized negative charge. For positive ions protolysis reduces the charge and entropy contributions will increase the acid strength. Although salvation effects make any rigorous analysis difficult but following trends have been observed: -

(i) **AH_n Compounds:** In them acid strength increases on moving from left to right in a period *e.g.*

$$CH_4 \ll NH_3 \ll H_2O \ll HF$$

This trend can be readily related to an increase in electro-negativity of the element attached to H.

Acid strength increases on moving down a group e.g., HF <HCl < HBr < HI

This trend is not an expected from electro-negativity. Changes of solvation are important, but the trend is in decreasing H – x bond strength down the group.

The **oxides of non-metals** are **acidic** and give **oxoacids** in water e.g., HNO_3, H_2SO_4 etc.

The **oxides of metals** are **basic.** However metals in high oxidation states can also form oxoacids.

(ii) The strength of **oxoacids** can be predicted by **Palling rules:-**

 (a) Writing the formula as $X O_p (OH)_q$, the pK_a depends largely on the values of p, being roughly equal to $(8 - 5p)$ irrespective of q. e.g.,

HOCl;	$p = 0$;	$pK_a = 7.2$
H_3PO_4;	$p = 1$;	$pK_a = 2.1$
H_2SO_4;	$p = 2$;	$pK_a = -2$
$HClO_4$;	$p = 3$;	$pK_a = -10$

 (b) For **polymeric acids,** pK_a increases by about five units for each subsequent protolysis step. e.g.,

$H_2PO_4^-$;	$pK_a = 7.4$
HPO_4^{2-};	$pK_a = 12.7$

The larger values of p give more scope for negative charge to be delocalized over the anion e.g., in ClO^- the formal charge is confined to one oxygen atom where as in ClO_4^- (only two of the four equivalent structures shown) is spread equally over four.

$$\left[\; Cl - O^- \qquad \overset{\displaystyle O}{\underset{\displaystyle O}{\overset{\|}{\underset{\|}{O = Cl - O^-}}}} \longleftrightarrow \overset{\displaystyle O}{\underset{\displaystyle O}{\overset{\|}{\underset{|}{O = Cl = O}}}} \; \right]$$

(iii) **Aqua cations:** Aqueous Fe^{3+} is stronger acid than HF.

Strongly acidic cations have either a high charge/size ratio (*e.g.*, Be^{2+}, Al^{3+}, Fe^{3+} etc) or are derived from metals with low electropositive character (*e.g.*, Hg^{2+}). Salts containing these ions form rather acidic solutions. Some of their compounds show amphoteric character and dissolve in alkaline solution to give oxoanions. e.g. $Al(OH)_3$

Al $(OH)_3$ is insoluble in neutral pH range

Al $(OH)_3$ dissolves at pH > 10 to form $[Al (OH)_4]^-$

5.3 Complex Formation

During formation of a complex in an aqueous solution, a ligand molecule or ion replaces solvating water molecules. Successive ligands may be attached, giving a stepwise formation (equilibrium) constants.

Although complex formation is quite characteristics of transition metal ions, but it is not confirmed to such ions only.

Stability of Co-ordination Compounds in Solution

The formation of a co-ordination compound involves reaction between a metal ion and ligands. If the force of attraction of the metal ion with ligands is strong a stable complex may result. Mostly the complex ions are highly stable. However, their possibility of dissociation in aqueous solutions cannot be ruled out completely though these may be dissociated to a small extent. Thus, a chemical equilibrium may be established between the undissociated complex and the dissociated ions.

$$(ML_n)^{b+} \rightleftharpoons M^{a+} + nL^{x-}$$

Here $a+, x$ and $b+$ are the charges on metal atoms, ligand and complex respectively. Thus, the equilibrium constant for the above reaction is given by the expression

$$K = \frac{[M^{a+}][L^{x-}]^n}{[(ML_n)^{b+}]}$$

The above equilibrium constant is called dissociation constant. Consequently, the smaller is the value of K, the greater is the stability of complex and *vice versa*.

The reciprocal of dissociation constant is called stability constant. The greater the value of the stability constant, the greater will be the stability of complex ion.

Alternatively, if the equilibrium is given as

$$M^{a+} + nL^{x-} \rightleftharpoons [ML_n]^{b+}$$

where $a+$, $x-$ and $b+$ have the usual significance, the equilibrium constant Ks, the stability constant of the complex is given as

$$K = \frac{[(ML_n)^{b+}]}{[(M^{a+})][L^{x-}]^n}$$

The magnitude of the stability constant gives an indication of the *stability of the complex* in solution. The values of Ks for a new complex in solution are given below:

System	Ks
$Cu^{2+} + 4NH_3 \rightleftharpoons [Cu(NH_3)_4]^{2+}$	4.5×10^{11}
$Cu^{2+} + 4CN^- \rightleftharpoons [Cu(CN)_4]^{2-}$	2.0×10^{27}

The values of Ks given above indicate that CN^- is a relatively stronger ligand than NH_3 and forms more stable complex.

Factors Affecting the Stability of Complex

The stability of a complex depends upon

(i) the nature of central ion and   (ii) the nature of ligand.

Several steps of complex formation may be possible, and the **successive equilibrium constants** for the reactions

$$M + L \longrightarrow ML$$
$$ML + L \longrightarrow ML_2$$

are known as the **stepwise formation constants K_1, K_2.....**

The over all equilibrium constant is given by

$$B_n = K_1 . K_2 . K_3 ..... K_n$$

Successive stepwise formation constants generally decrease regularly $K_1 > K_2 > K_3$ .... of the maximum value being determined by the number of ligands that can be accommodated. This is generally six (except for chelating ligands). The decrease can be understood in terms of entropy consideration as successive ligand has one less place available to attach.

Always remember that each ligand replaces one or more solvating water molecules.

Hard and Soft Behaviour

In case of cation of metals of early groups of periodic table, the complexing strength with halide ions is in the following order

$$F^- >> Cl^- > Br^- > I^-$$

In case of later transition metals and post-transition metal the above trend is reversed. (e.g., Pt^{2+}, Hg^{2+}, Pb^{2+}). The former behaviour is known as **class a** and the latter is known as **class b** behaviour. The two differ in **hard** and **soft** properties. **Class b** form strong complexes with such ligands as ammonia (which are softer than water) and the **class a** ions do not form complex with such ligands particularly in water.

Trends in **bond strength** show that almost every ion would follow the **class a** sequence in the gas phase, and the behaviour in water is partly because of due to weaker solvation of larger anions. With **class b** ions bond strengths decrease slowly $Hg–F > Hg–Cl > Hg–Br.....$ then do the solvation energies of the halide ions. However, in case of **class a** ions, the change in bond strengths is more marked than that of solvation energies.

Class b complex formation is **enthalpy dominant** whereas **class a** complex formation is **entropy dominant.**

Some polyatomic ions (NO_3^-, ClO_4^-, PF_6^- etc.) have very low complexing power to either **class a** or **class b** metals. Such ions are quite useful to study the thermodynamic properties of metal ions.

Chelats and Macro Molecules

Chelating ligands generally form stronger complexes and are useful for analysis of metal ions by **complexometric titration's** and in removing toxic metals in case of personing.

H₂N   NH₂

ethylenediamme
(bidentate)

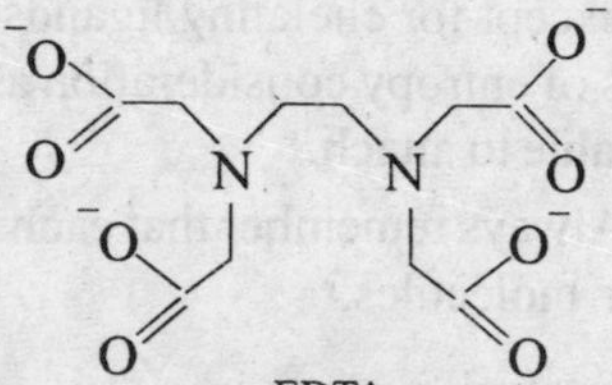

EDTA
(hexa dentate)

The **origin of chelate effect** in entropic.

The **length of chain formed** between ligand atoms is important in chelate formation, the most stable complexes are generally formed with four atoms (including the donors) so that with the metal ion a five numbered ring is formed.

Small ring sizes are less favourable due to **bond angles** involved; larger ones are less favourable due to increased **configuration entropy** of the complex.

Limiting the possibility of bond rotation increases the complexing power even with optimum ring sizes. Thus phenanthroline forms stronger complex than tripyridyl.

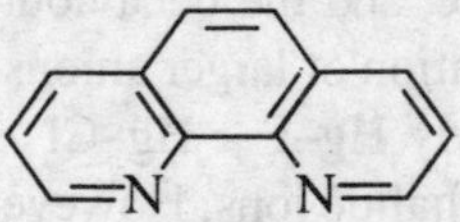

(Phenanthroline) 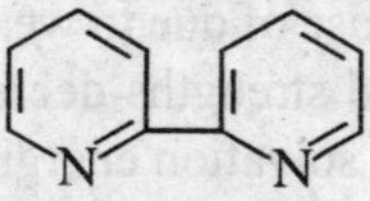   (Bipyridyl)

A reduction of configurational entropy is important in case of **macrocyclic ligands** in which several donor atoms are already "tied" by a molecular frame-work into the optimal position of complex formation (*e.g.,* **crown ethers** such as 18-crown– 6, 5) and bicyclic **cryptands** such as [2, 2, 1 – crypt, 6].

The complex strength increases (as expected) and the resulting **macrocyclic effect** permits formation of complexes having ions as those of group 1 metals, which otherwise have very low complexing power.

Size selectivity is another feature of **macrocyclic ligands**. The size selectivity corresponds to different cavity sizes and it can be altered by varying the ring size.

Chelating and **macrocyclic** effects are important in biological chemistry.

pH changes also effect the formation of complexes in a large number of cases.

5.4 Solubility of Ionic Substances

Let us consider the thermodynamics of a solid that involves in water as follows

$$Mn\, Xm\, (B) = n\, M^{m+}\, (or) + m\, x^{n-}\, (or)$$

The equilibrium constant is then given by

$$K_{sp} = [M^{m+}]^n\, [X^{n-}]^m$$

The equilibrium constant for dissolving the ionic substances is known as **solubility product (K_{sp})**.

According to Thermodynamics

$$\Delta G^\circ = -RT \ln K$$

K_{sp} is related to ΔG° of solution.

Following diagram illustrates the thermodynamic cycle that relates the over all ΔG to two separate steps

(i)   the formation of gas phase ions, and

(ii) solvation of these gas phase ions.

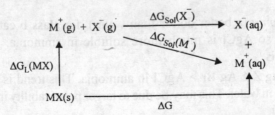

Fig. 5.1 Thermodynamic cycle for the solution of ionic solid Mx.

Major trends in solubilities in water

(i)   Soluble salts are generally those which have ions of very difficult size. Thus Li salts are least soluble (in group 1 cation) in the series with OH⁻ and F⁻, but most soluble with larger cations (*e.g.*, Cl^-, NO_3^-).

(ii) Salts in which both the ions carry multiple charge are likely to be less soluble than ones with single charge.

(iii) With ions of different charges, insoluble compounds are formed when the lower charged ion is smaller.

(iv) Lower solubility may result due to covalent contributions to the lattice energy.

Influence of pH and Complexing

The influence of pH as solubility is seen in case one of the ions has significant Bronsted acid or base properties.

Metal oxides and hydroxides dissolve in acids and they may be precipitated from a solution containing a metal ion as the pH is increased.

Any ligand that complexes with metal ion will increase the solubility.

Other Solvents

The HF and H_2SO_4 are two other solvents that have a polarity. The trends in solubility of metal fluorides in HF are quite similar to those for hydroxides and oxides in water. Thus they follow the sequence $MF > MF_2 > MF_3$.

For a given charge the solubility tends to increase with cation size.

Ammonia (a better donor than water), for **class b** cations (*e.g.*, Ag^+) and so AgCl is much more soluble in ammonia. The trend observed is

Ag Z > Ag Br > AgCl in ammonia. This trend is reverse of that found in water. This may be due to larger polarizability in ammonia than water.

5.5 Electrode Potentials

Electrode potential is a measure of the thermodynamics of a redox reaction. It may be expressed as the difference between two half-cell potentials.

The electrical potential difference set up between the metal and solution of its ions is known as **half-cell electrode potential.** In fact, it is the measure of the tendency of an electrode in a half-cell to lose or gain electrons.

The electrochemical cell consists of two half-cells. The electrodes in these half-cells have different electrode potentials. When the circuit is completed the loss of electrons occurs at the electrode having lower reduction potential whereas the gain of electrons occurs at the electrode with higher reduction potential. The difference in the electrode potentials of the two electrodes of the cell is called **electromotive force** (abbreviated as **EMF**) or **cell voltage**. Mathematically, it can be expressed as

$$EMF = E_{Red}(Cathode) - E_{Red}(Anode) \text{ or simply as } EMF = E_{Cathode} - E_{Anode}$$

Since in the representation of a cell, the cathode is written on right hand side and the anode on left hand side, therefore, EMF of a cell is also sometimes written as:

$$EMF = E_{Right} - E_{Left} = E_R - E_L$$

EMF of the cell may be defined as the *potential difference between the two terminals of the cell when either no or very little current is drawn from it.* It is measured with the help of potentiometer or vacuum tube voltmeter.

The cell potential E is related to free energy change by the relation

$$\boxed{\Delta G = -nFE}$$

where F is **Faraday Constant** $(9.6485 \times 10^4 \text{ C mol}^{-1})$ and n is number of electrons passed per mole of reaction.

Direction of Reaction

For a cell to be functional

$E_{cell} = E_{Cathode} - E_{Anode}$ should be positive.

For calculation of E we make use of **Nernst equation** given below

$$E = E^\circ + \frac{nR}{nF} \ln \frac{[OX]}{[Red]}$$

When reaction involves H^+ or OH^- ions, these must be included in Nernst equation to predict **pH dependence** of the couple. Thus for the MnO_4^-/Mn^{2+} half-cell reaction, a factor of $[H^+]^8$ should be included in the [OX] terms, leading to reduction of potential of $8/5 \times 0.059 = 0.094U$ per unit increase in pH.

Potential also get influenced by **complex formation**. Potential increases if lower oxidation state is more strongly complexed and if the ligand complexes more strongly with higher oxidation state it reduces the potential.

Latimer Diagram. It shows the standard electrode potentials associated with different oxidation states of an element.

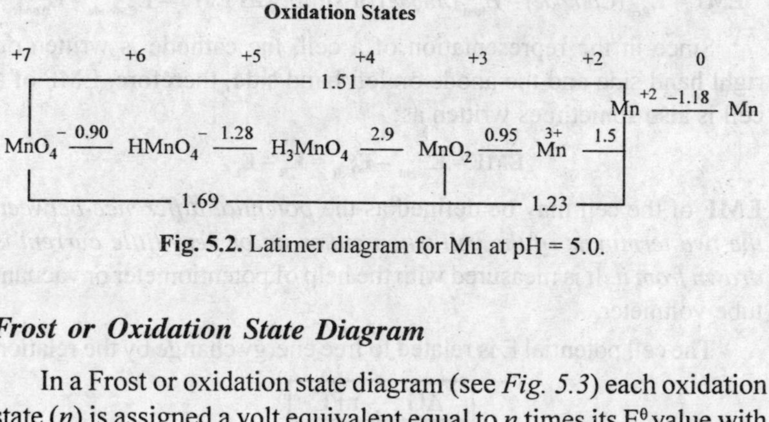

Oxidation States

| +7 | +6 | +5 | +4 | +3 | +2 | 0 |

$$MnO_4^- \xrightarrow{-0.90} HMnO_4^- \xrightarrow{1.28} H_3MnO_4 \xrightarrow{2.9} MnO_2 \xrightarrow{0.95} Mn^{3+} \xrightarrow{1.5} Mn^{2+} \xrightarrow{-1.18} Mn$$

(with overbracket links: 1.51 from $+6$ to MnO_2; 1.69 from MnO_4^- to Mn^{3+}; 1.23 from MnO_2 to Mn^{2+})

Fig. 5.2. Latimer diagram for Mn at pH = 5.0.

Frost or Oxidation State Diagram

In a Frost or oxidation state diagram (see *Fig. 5.3*) each oxidation state (n) is assigned a volt equivalent equal to n times its E^θ value with respect to the element. The potential E^θ in volts between any two-oxidation states is equal to the slope of the line between the points in this diagram. Steep positive slopes show strong oxidizing agents, steep negative slopes strong reducing agents. Frost diagrams are convenient for displaying the comparative redox properties of elements.

Frost diagrams also provide a visual guide to when disproportionation of a species is expected. For example, in *Fig. 5.3* the Mn^{3+} state at pH = 0 is found above the line formed by joining Mn^{2+} with MnO_2. It follows that the Mn^{3+}/Mn^{2+} potential is more positive than MnO_2/Mn^{3+}, and disproportionation is predicted:

$$2Mn^{3-}(aq) + 2H_2O \longrightarrow MnO_2(s) + Mn^{2+}(aq) + 4H^+(aq)$$

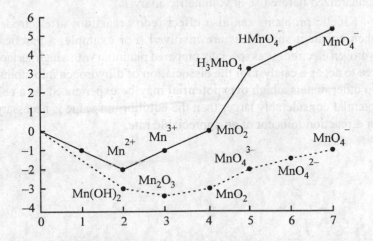

Fig. 5.3. Frost diagram for Mn at pH = 0 (solid line) and pH = 14 (dashed line).

The equilibrium constant of this reaction can be calculated by noting that it is made up from the half reactions for MnO_2/Mn^{3+} and Mn^{3+}/Mn^{2+} each with n = 1, and has $E^\theta = 1.5 - 0.95 = 0.55$ V from *Fig. Latimer Diagram,* giving $K = 2 \times 10^9$. The states Mn^v and Mn^{vt} are similarly unstable to disproportionate at pH = 0, whereas at pH = 14, also shown in *Fig. Frost Diagram,* only Mn^v will disproportionate.

Latimer and **Frost** diagrams display the same information but in a different way. When interpreting electrode potential data, either in numerical or graphical form, it is important to remember that a single potential in isolation has no meaning.

Kinetic Limitations

Electrode potentials are thermodynamic quantities and show nothing about how fast a redox reaction can take place. Simple electron transfer reactions (as in Mn^{3+}/Mn^{2+}) are expected to be rapid, but redox reactions where covalent bonds are made or broken may be much slower. For example, the MnO_4^-/MnO_2 potential is well above that for the oxidation of water (see O_2/H_2O in *Table* 5.1), but the predicted reaction happens very slowly and aqueous permanganate is commonly used as an oxidizing agent (although it should always be standardized before use in volumetric analysis).

Kinetic problems can also effect redox reactions at electrodes when covalent substances are involved. For example, a practical hydrogen electrode uses specially prepared platinum with a high surface area to act as a catalyst for the dissociation of dihydrogen into atoms. On other metals a high **overpotential** may be experienced, as a cell potential considerably larger than the equilibrium value is necessary for a reaction to occur at an appreciable rate.

6

Chemistry of Non-Metals

6.1 Introduction to Non-Metals

Introduction. From the discussion on chemical families and periodic properties, it is obvious that the separation of elements into metals and non-metals is not clear cut and without ambiguity. The fairly obvious division between metals and non-metals is shown by a thick steeped line in the following shortened figure of the modern periodic table. Some of the elements next to the thick steps, such as germanium, arsenic and antimony have similarities to both metals and non-metals and are named *metalloids (or semi metals)*.

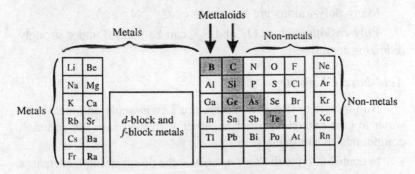

Fig. 6.1. Classification of elements as metals, non-metals and metalloids on the basis of conductance.

Non-metallic elements include hydrogen and the upper right hand portion of *p-block*.

Covalent Chemistry

Covalent chemistry is the characteric property of non-metals. **Hydrogen** can form only one covalent bond and in **boron** compounds we find an incomplete octet.

The covalency falls with group member and variable valency is observed in a number of these non-metals. The maximum possible oxidation state increases from +5 in group 15 to +8 in group 18.

Octet expansion or **hyper-valent state** is due to the involvement of d-orbitals of the same principal quantum shell (*e.g.,* 3d in 3rd period, 4d in fourth period etc). The two other factors that play a role in octet expansion are

(i) larger size of the elements in lower periods which allow higher coordination number, and

(ii) lower electro negativity values of elements in the lower periods, which accommodate positive formal charge more easily.

Due to these the behaviour of elements of 3 period differs from those of the elements in the lower periods.

Period 2 elements do not readily form multiple bonds where others form such bonds readily (*e.g.,* C, N, O etc).

Ionic Chemistry. Only the most electronegative elements form simple mono atomic ions (*e.g.* O^{2-}, Cl^-.).

Many **poly-anions** are known (*e.g.,* C_2^{2-}, N_3^- etc).

Poly-cations such as O_2^+ and S_4^{2+} can be formed under strongly oxidizing conditions.

Acid-base Chemistry

Non-metals oxides and halides are **Lewis acids** and react with water to give **oxoacids**, which together with their salts are common compounds of non-metals.

In contribution with '*hard acceptor*' the donor strength decreases down a group N > P > As but with '*soft acceptor*' the trend may be reversed.

Ion-transfer reactions. Such reaction result in formation of complex ions (*e.g.*, NH_4^+, H_3O^+, NH_2^-, OH^- etc) halide complex (PCl_4^+, SF_5^- etc.) and oxoanions and cations (SO_4^{2-}, NO_2^+ etc.)

Bronsted basicity follows the order

$$NH_3 > H_2O > HF \text{ and } NH_3 > PH_3 > AsH_3$$

Redox Chemistry

O, F, Cl, Br are good oxidizing agents. Oxidizing power increases with group number and reducing power decreases.

Compounds of $As^{(v)}$, $Se^{(VI)}$ and Br^{VII} in period 4 are more strongly oxidizing than corresponding and S in period 3 and 5. This **alternation effect** can be related to irregular trends in isolation energy.

6.2 Hydrogen

Hydrogen is the commonest element found in the Universe and is a major constituent of stars. It is relatively much less common on Earth but nevertheless it forms nearly 1% by mass of the crust and oceans, mainly as **water** and in hydrates and hydroxide minerals of the crust. It is ubiquitous in biology.

The **dihydrogen molecule H_2** is the stable form of the element under normal conditions, although atomic hydrogen can be made in the gas phase at high temperatures, and hydrogen may become a metallic solid or liquid at extremely high pressures. At 1 bar pressure, dihydrogen condenses to a liquid at 20 K and solidifies at 14 K, these being the lowest boiling and melting points for any substance except helium. The H–H bond has a length of 74 pm and a dissociation enthalpy of 436 kJ mol^{-1}. This is the shortest bond known, and one of the strongest single covalent bonds. Although it is thermodynamically capable of reacting with many elements and compounds, these reactions generally have a large kinetic barrier and need elevated temperatures and/or the use of catalysts.

Dihydrogen is an important industrial chemical, mostly made from the **steam re-forming** of hydrocarbons from petroleum and natural gas. The simplest of these reactions,

$$Ch_4 + H_2O \longrightarrow CO + 3H_2$$

It is endothermic, and temperatures around 1400 K is required to shift the equilibrium to the right. Major uses of hydrogen are in the synthesis of ammonia, the hydrogenation of vegetable fats to make margarine, and the production of organic chemicals and hydrogen chloride.

Hydrides of Nonmetals

Hydrogen forms molecular compounds with nonmetallic elements. *Table* 6.1 lists some of these. With the exception of the boranes hydrogen always forms a single covalent bond. Complexities of formula or structure arise from the possibility of **catenation**, direct element-element bonds as in hydrogen peroxide, H–O–O–H, and in many organic compounds. The International Union of Pure and Applied Chemistry (IUPAC) has suggested systematic names ending in-ane, but for many hydrides 'trivial' names are still generally used. In addition to binary compounds, there are many others with several elements present. These include nearly all organic compounds elements and in organic compounds such as hydroxylamine, H_2NOH. The **substitutive system** of naming inorganic compounds derived from hydrides is similar to the nomenclature used in organic chemistry (*e.g.* chlorosilane, SiH_3Cl).

Table 6.1 shows the bond strengths and the standard free energies of formation of hydrides. Bond strengths and thermodynamic stabilities decrease down each group. Compounds such as boranes and silanes are strong reducing agents and may inflame spontaneously in air. Reactivity generally increases with catenation.

Table 6.1. A selection of nonmetal hydrides (E indicates nonmetal)

Hydride formulae and names		Normal boiling point (°C)	E-H bond enthalpy (kJ mol⁻¹)	ΔG_f^{θ} (kJ mol⁻¹ at 298 K)
B	B_2H_6 diborane	-93	—	+87
C	CH_4 methane	-162	413	-51
	C_2H_6 ethane	-89	—	-33
	C_2H_4 ethane	-104	—	+68

Hydride formulae and names		Normal boiling point (°C)	E-H bond enthalpy (kJ mol⁻¹)	ΔG_f^0 (kJ mol⁻¹) at 298 K)
Si	SiH_4 silane	-112	318	+57
	Si_2H_5 disilane	-14	—	+127
Ge	GeH_4 germane	-88	285	+113
N	NH_3 ammonia (azane)[a]	-33	391	-17
	N_2H_4 hydrazine (dizane)[a]	113	—	+149
	HN_3 hydrozen azide	36[b]	—	+327
P	PH_3 phosphine (phosphane)[a]	-88	321	+13
	P_2H_4 diphosphane	64[b]	—	—
As	AsH_3 arsine (arsane)[a]	-55	296	69
O	H_2O water (oxidane)[a]	100	464	-237
	H_2O_2 hydrogen peroxide (dioxidane)[a]	152	—	-120
S	H_2S hydrogen sulfide (sulfane)[a]	-60	364	-34
	H_2S_2 disulfane	70[b]	—	—
Se	H_2Se hydrogen selenide (selane)[a]	-42	313	+16
F	HF hydrogen fluoride	19	568	-297
Cl	HCl hydrogen chloride	-85	432	-95
Br	HBr hydrogen bromine	-68	366	-53
I	HI hydrogen iodide	-35	289	+2

[a]IUPAC recommended systematic names that are already used.
[b]Extrapolated values for compounds decomposing before boiling at atmospheric pressure.

General Methods of Preparation Hydrides

(i) direct combination of elements:

$$N_2 + 3H_2 \longrightarrow 2NH_3$$

(ii) reaction of a metal compound of the element with a protonic acid such as water:

$$CaP_2 + 6H_2O \longrightarrow 2PH_3 + 3Ca(OH)_2$$

(iii) reduction of a halide or oxide with $LiAH_4$ or $NaBH_4$:

$$3NaBH_4 + 4BF_3 \longrightarrow 2B_2H_6 + 3NaBF_4$$

Reactions (ii) or (iii) is needed when direct combination is thermodynamically unfavourable. Catenated hydrides can generally be formed by controlled pyrolysis of the mononuclear compound.

Brensted acidity arises from the possibility transferring a proton to a base, which may be the same compound. Basicity is possible when nonbonding electron pairs are present. Basicity towards protons decreases towards the right and down each group in the periodic table, so that ammonia is the strongest base among simple hydrides.

Compounds with Metals

Not all metallic elements form hydrides. Those that do can be classified as follows:

(i) Highly electropositive metals form solid hydrides generally regarded as containing the H^- ion. They have structures similar to halides, although the ionic character of hydrides is undoubtedly much lower. Examples are LiH (rocksalt structure) and MgH_2.

(ii) Some d- and f-block elements form hydrides that are generally metallic in nature, and of variable (nonstoichiometric) composition. Examples are TiH_2 and CeH_{2+x}.

(iii) Some heavier p-block metals form molecular hydrides similar to those of non-metals in the same group, examples are **digallane** (Ga_2H_6) and **stannane** (SnH_4), both of very slow stability.

Hydrides of more electropositive elements can be made by direct reaction between elements. They are very strong reducing agents and react with water to give dihydrogen:

$$CaH_2 + 2H_2O \longrightarrow Ca(OH)_2 + 2H_2$$

The hydrides ion can act as a ligand and form **hydride complexes** similar in some ways to those of halides, although their stability is mostly limited by the reducing properties of the H^- ion. The most important complexes are the tetrahedral ions BH_4^- and AlH_4^- normally found as the salts $NaBH_4$ and $LiAlH_4$. They may be made by the action of NaH or LiH on a halide or similar compound of B or Al, and are used as reducing agents and for the preparation of hydrides of other elements.

Many transition metal complexes containing hydrogen are known, including the unusual nine-coordinate ion $[ReH_9]^{2-}$. Hydride is a very strong s-donor ligand and is often found in conjunction with π-acid ligand and in organometallic compounds.

The Hydrogen Bond

A hydrogen atom bound to an electronegative atom such as N, O or F may interact in a noncovalent way with another electronegative atom. The resulting **hydrogen bond** has an energy in the range 10-60 kJ mol^{-1}, weak by standards of covalent bounds but strong compared with other intermolecular forces. The strongest hydrogen bonds are formed when a fluoride ion is involved, example in the symmetrical $[F–H–F]^*$ ion. Symmetrical bonds are some times formed with oxygen but in most cases the hydrogen is not symmetrically disposed, a typical example being in liquid water where the normal O–H bond has a length of 96 pm and the hydrogen bond a length around 250 pm. Hydrogen bonding arises from a combination of electrostatic (ion-dipole and dipole-dipole) forces and orbital overlap; the latter effect may be treated by a three-centre molecular orbital approach.

Hydrogen bonding is crucial for the secondary structure of biological molecules such as proteins and nucleic acids, and for the operation of the genetic code. Its influence can be seen in the boiling points of simple hydrides. The exceptional values for NH_3, H_2O and HF result from strong hydrogen bonding in the liquid.

Deuterium and Tritium

Deuterium (^2D) and tritium (^3T) are heavier isotopes of hydrogen. The former is stable and makes up about 0.015% of all normal hydrogen. Its physical and chemical properties are slightly different from those of the light isotope ^1H. For example, in the electrolysis of water H is evolved faster and this allows fairly pure D_2 to be prepared. Tritium is a radioactive β-emitter with a half-life of 12.35 years, and is made when some elements are bombarded with neutrons. Both isotopes are used for research purposes. They also undergo very exothermic **nuclear fusion reactions**, which form the basis for thermonuclear weapons ('hydrogen bombs') and could possibly be used as a future energy source.

Their relative abundance of various isotopes of hydrogen in nature is as follows:

$$H : D : T : : 5000 : 1 : 10^{-17}$$

The scarcity of tritium is due to the instability and consequent radioactivity of its nucleus.

On electrolysis of water, the lighter isotope of hydrogen is evolved first. The smaller residue of water left is richer in the heavier isotope and is called *heavy water* or deuterium oxide (D_2O). On electrolysis of about 20 liters of water only 1 cm^3 of heavy water is obtained. Deuterium is obtained by electrolysis of heavy water or its decomposition with sodium or red-hot iron.

$$2D_2O \xrightarrow{\text{Electrolysis}} \underset{\text{(At cathole)}}{2D_2} + \underset{\text{(At anode)}}{O_2}$$

$$2D_2O + 2Na \longrightarrow \underset{\substack{\text{Sodium} \\ \text{deuteroxide}}}{2NaOD} + \underset{\text{Deuterium}}{D_2}$$

Properties of Deuterium. Properties of deuterium are similar to those of protium. For example, it is colourless, odourless and tasteless. It is insoluble in water and bad conductor of heat. Its atomicity is 2. Some other physical constants these isotopes are:

Property	Protium	Deuterium
B.P. (K)	20.38	23.59
M.P. (K)	13.95	18.65
Latent heat of fusion (J mol^{-1})	117	218

In general properties of isotopes are qualitatively very similar but there is quantitative difference especially when the percentage difference in mass is appreciable. *Property differences due to difference in mass are called* **isotope effects.**

In chemical reactions protium and deuterium show quantitative difference due to isotope effects. For example, ionization of water is five times the ionization of heavy water. Rate of breaking of H–H bonds is 18 times the rate of breaking of D–D bonds. Similarly, rate of reaction between H_2 and Cl_2 is 13.4 times the rate of reaction between D_2 and Cl_2.

For elements heavier than hydrogen the isotope effect is much smaller because the percentage difference in mass is very small. For example, $\frac{127}{53}I$ reacts only 102 times faster than $\frac{129}{53}I$ and the properties are nearly the same.

During electrolysis of water, H–O bonds break faster than D–O bonds and we get only protium in the beginning leaving heavy water behind.

6.3 Boron

It is relatively rare though it occurs as borates, which have similar structure as silicates. In combined state it occurs as salts of boric acid. For example, **Basic acid (H_3BO_3), Borax ($Na_2B_4O_7.10\ H_2O$), Boracite ($2Mg_3\ B_8O_{15}.\ Mgcl_2$), coleurnite ($Ca_2B_6O_{11}.5H_2O$), Kernite** or **Borozite** ($Na_2B_4O_7.4H_2O$).

It is the only non-metallic element in group 13 that has a tendency to form covalent bonds. Its simple compounds BCl_3, BF_3 etc, are *electron deficient* (have less than 8 electrons) and so are **Lewis acids.** However, boron accommodates its electron deficiency by forming clusters with multi-centre bonding.

It is used widely as borates in glasses, enamels, detergents and cosmetics, and in lesser amounts in metallurgy.

Boron is not required in its elemental form, but it can be obtained by electrolysis of fused salts, or by reduction either of B_2O_3 with electropositive metals or of a halide with dihydrogen, the last method giving the purest boron. The element has many allotropic structures of great complexity; their dominant theme is the presence of icosahedral B_{12} units connected in different ways. Multicentre bonding models are required to interpret these structures.

Hydrides

The simplest hydrogen compounds are salts of the **tetrahydroborate** ion BH_4^- which is tetrahedral and isoelectronic with methane (see Topic CI). $LiBH_4$ is prepared by reducing BF_3, with LiH. It is more widely used as the sodium salt, which is a powerful reducing agent having sufficient kinetic stability to be used in aqueous solution. Reaction of $NaBH_4$ with either I_2 or BF_3 in diglyme $(CH_3OCH_2)_2O$ gives diborane B_2H_6, the simplest molecular hydride. Its structure with bridging hydrogen atoms required three-centre two-electron bonds.

$$2NaBH_4 + 2I_2 \longrightarrow B_2H_6 + 2NaI + 2HI$$

Heating B_2H_6 above 100°C leads to pyrolysis and generates a variety of more complex boranes of which tetraborane(10) B_4H_{10} and decabornae(14) $B_{10}H_{14}$ are the most stable. Other reactions can lead to anionic species, such as the icosahedral dodecahydrodecaborate (2-) $[B_{12}H_{12}]^{2-}$, prepared at 180°C:

$$5B_2H_6 + 2NaBH_4 \longrightarrow Na_2[B_{12}H_{12}] + 13H_2$$

boranes with heteroatoms can also be prepared, $B_{10}C_2H_{12}$, which is isoelectronic with $[B_{12}H_{12}]^{2-}$.

Boranes are strong reducing agents and the neutral molecules, inflame spontaneously in air, although the anions $[B_nH_n]^{2-}$ have remarkable kinetic stability. Diborane itself reacts with Lewis bases to give donor-acceptor complexes with BH_3, which is a 'soft' Lewis acid and forms adducts with soft bases such as CO (1). More complex products often result from unsymmetrical cleavage of B_2H_6, for example,

$$B_2H_6 + 2NH_3 \longrightarrow [NH_3BH_2NH_3]^+[BH_4]^-$$

$$^+O \equiv C - \overset{-}{B} \overset{\displaystyle H}{\underset{\displaystyle H}{\cdots H}}$$

1

Halides

Molecular BX_3 compounds are formed with all halogens. They have the trigonal planar structure predicts by VSEPR although there appears to be a certain degree of π bonding (strongest in BF_3) involving halogen lone-pairs and the empty boron 2p orbital (see **2** for one of the possible resonance forms). The halides are strong Lewis acids, BF_3 and BCl_3 being used as catalysts (*e.g.*, in organic Friedel-Crafts acylations). Interaction with a donor gives a tetrahedral geometry around boron as with the analogous BH_3 complex **1**. The π bonding in the parent molecule is lost and for this reason BF_3, where such bonding is strongest, is more resistant to adopting the tetrahedral geometry than are the heavier halides. Thus the acceptor strengths follow the order

$$BF_3 < BCl_3 < BBr_3 > BI_3$$

which is the reverse of that found with halides of most other elements.

$$^+F = \bar{B} \overset{\displaystyle F}{\underset{\displaystyle B}{\diagup}}$$

2

Strongest interaction occurs with hard donors such as F^- (forming the stable tetrafluoroborate ion $[BF_4]^-$) and with oxygen donors such as water. Except with BF_3 (where the B–F bonds are very strong) complex formation often leads to solvolysis, forming $B(OH)_3$ in water.

Pyrolysis of BX_3 compounds leads to halides with B–B bonds, for example, B_2X_4 (**3** with X = F or Cl) and polyhedral B_nCl_n molecules (n = 4, 8, 9).

$$
\begin{array}{ccc}
F & & F \\
\diagdown & & \diagup \\
& B - B & \\
\diagup & & \diagdown \\
F & & F
\end{array}
$$

3

Oxygen Compounds

Boric oxide B_2O_3 is very hard to crystallize, the glass has a linked covalent network in which both bridging B–O–B and terminal B = 0 bonds may be present. The hydoxide boric acid $B(OH)_3$ is formed by the hydrolysis of many boron compounds. It has a layer structure made up of planar molecules linked by hydrogen bonding. It is a Lewis acid that acts as a Bronsted acid in protic solvents. In water the equilibrium

$$B(OH)_3 + 2H_2O \; B(OH)_4^- + H_3O^+$$

gives a $pK_4 = 9.25$ but complexing can increase the acidity; for example, in anhydrous H_2SO_4 it forms $[B(HSO_4)_4]^-$ and is one of the few species that can act as a strong acid in that solvent.

Borates can be formed with all metals, although those of groups 1 and 2 are best known. The structural features are complex and rival those of silicates (see Topic D5). Boron can occur as planar BO_3 or tetrahedral BO_4 groups, often linked by B–O–B bonds as in silicates. For example, **4** shows the ion found in borax $Na_2[B_4O_5(OH)_4].8H_2O$, where both three and four coordinate boron is present. **Borosilicate glasses** (such as 'Pyrex') have lower coefficients of thermal expansion than pure silicate glasses and so are more resistant to thermal shock.

4

Other Compounds

Boron forms many compounds with nitrogen. Some of these are structurally analogous to carbon compounds, the pair of atoms BN being isoelectronic with CC. (For example, the ion $[NH_3BH_2NH_3]^+$ is analogous to propane, $CH_3CH_2CH_3$). **Boron nitride** BN can form two solid structures, one containing hexagonal BN layers similar to graphite, and the other with tetrahedral sp^3 bonding like diamond. **Borazine** $B_3N_3H_6$ has a 6-π-electron ring like benzene (**5** shows one resonance form; see Topic C6). Although BN is very hard and resistant to chemical attack, borazine is much more reactive than benzene and does not undergo comparable electrophilic substitution reactions. The difference is a result of the polar B–N bond, and the more reactive B–H bonds.

$$
\begin{array}{ccc}
 & H & \\
 & | & \\
H & B & \\
\ \ \backslash N & \diagup \ \backslash & N \diagup H \\
 & \| & \\
H \diagup B & N & B \diagdown H \\
 & | & \\
 & H & \\
 & 5 & \\
\end{array}
$$

Boron forms a binary carbide, often written B_4C but actually nonstoichiometry, and compounds with most metals. The stoichiometrics and structures of these solids mostly defy simple interpretation. Many types of chains, layers and polyhedra of boron atoms are found. Simple examples are CaB_6 and UB_{12}, containing linked octahedra and icosahedra, respectively.

6.4 Carbon, Silicon and Germanium

Carbon occurs in free form of coal, graphite and diamond. It also occurs in nature as (O_2) as carbonate of metals $(MgCO_3, CaCO_3)$, which constitute sedimentary rocks. Carbon is important constituent of petroleum and all living organism.

Silicon is also as silicate and the earth's crust is made of complex silicates containing $-Si-O-Si-O-$ linkage. Silica (SiO_2) occurs in nature in many forms such as **quartz, rock, crystal sand, sound stone, flint** etc.

Germanium has some stable divalent compounds.

Of the three only carbon forms multiple bonds, and the compounds show many differences in structure and properties from those of Si and Ge.

The abundances of the elements by mass in the crust are: C about 480 p.p.m., Si 27% (second only to oxygen), and Ge 2 p.p.m. Carbon is important in the atmosphere and is the major element of life. Germanium is widely but thinly distributed in silicate and sulfide minerals.

All three elements can crystallize in the tetrahedrally bonded **diamond structure.** Si and Ge are semiconductors. Carbon has other allotropes. **Graphite** is the thermodynamically stable form at ordinary pressures, diamond at high pressures. More recently discovered forms include **buckminsterfullerene** C_{60}, higher fullerenes such as C_{70} and **nanotubes** composed of graphite sheets rolled into cylinders. In these structures carbon forms three σ bonds, the remaining valence electron being in delocalized π orbitals analogous to those in benzene.

The elements can be obtained by reduction of oxides or halides. Highly divide carbon black is used as a catalyst and black pigment, and impure carbon (coke) for reducing some metal oxides (*e.g.,* in the manufacture of iron; see Topic B4). Pure silicon prepared by reduction of $SiCl_4$ with Mg is used in electronics ('silicon chips') although much larger quantities of impure Si are used in steels.

Hydrides and Organic Compounds

Compounds of carbon with hydrogen and other elements form the vast area of organic chemistry. **Silanes** and **germanes** are Si and Ge analogous of methane and short-chain saturated hydrocarbons, and can be prepared by various methods, such as reduction of halides with $LiAlH_4$:

$$ECl_4 + LiAlH_4 \longrightarrow EH_4 + LiAlCl_4 \ (E = Si \ or \ Ge)$$

They are much more reactive than corresponding carbon compounds and will inflame spontaneously in air. Stability decreases with chain length in series such as

$$EH_4 > E_2H_6 > E_3H_8 > \dots$$

Many derivatives can be prepared where H is replaced by monofunctional groups such as halides, alkyl, $-NH_2$. Many Si and Ge compounds are similar in structure of those of carbon, but trisilylamine $(SiH_3)_3N$ and its germanium analog differ from $(CH_3)_3N$ in being nonbasic and having a geometry that is planar rather than pyramidal about N. This suggests the involvement of the N lone-pair electrons in partial multiple bonding through the valence expansion of Si or Ge.

Si and Ge analogs of compounds where carbon forms double bonds are much difficult to make. $(CH_3)_2SiO$ is not like propanone $(CH_3)_2C = 0$, but forms silicone **polymers** with rings or chains having single Si–O bonds (**1**). Attempts to make alkene analogs $R_2Si = SiR_2$ (where **R** is an organic group) generally result in single-bonded oligomers, except with very bulky R– groups such as mesityl $(2,4,6(CH_3)_3C_6H_2-)$, which prevent polymerization.

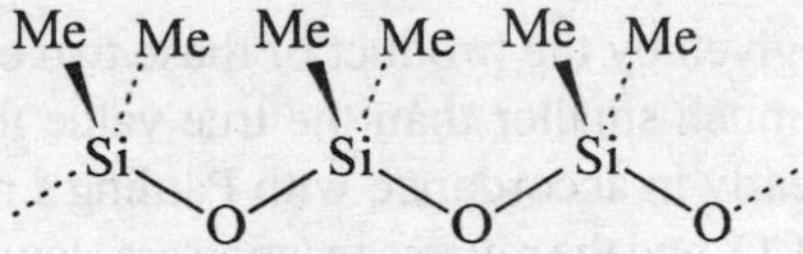

1

Halides

All halides EX_4 form tetrahedral molecules. Mixed halides are known, as well as fully or partially halogen-substituted catenated alkanes, silanes and germanes (*e.g.*, Ge_2Cl_6). Unlike the carbon compounds, halides of Si and Ge are Lewis acids and readily form complexes such as $[SiF_6]^{2-}$. Attack by Lewis bases often leads to decomposition, and thus rapid hydrolysis in water, unlike carbon halides, which are kinetically more inert.

Divalent halides EX_2 can be made as reactive gas-phase species, but only for Ge are stable noncatenarted Ge^{II} compounds formed. They have polymeric structures with pyramidal coordination as with Sn^{II}. The compound CF formed by reaction of fluorine and graphite has one F atom bonded to every C, thus disrupting the π bonding in the graphic layer but retaining the σ bonds and giving tetrahedral geometry about carbon. (Bromine forms intercalation compounds with graphite.

Oxygen Compounds

Whereas carbon forms the molecular oxides CO and CO_2 with multiple bonding, stable oxides of Si and Ge are polymeric. Silica SiO_2 has many structural forms based on networks of corner-sharing SiO_4 tetrahedra. GeO_2 can crystallize in silica-like structures as well as the rutile structure with six-coordinate Ge. This structure is stable for SiO_2 only at very high pressures, the difference being attributable to the greater size of Ge. Thermodynamically unstable solids SiO and GeO can be made but readily disproportionate to the ioxide.

CO_2 is fairly soluble in water but true carbonic acid is present in only low concentration:

$$CO_2(a) + H_2O = H_2CO_3 \qquad\qquad K = 16 \times 10^{-3}$$
$$H_2CO_3 + H_2O = HCO_3^- + H_3O^+ \qquad\qquad K = 25 \times 10^{-4}$$

The apparent K, given by the product of these two equilibria is 4.5×10^{-7} ($pK_a = 6.3$), much smaller than the true value for carbonic acid, which is more nearly in accordance with Pauling's rules ($pK_a = 3.6$). The hydration of CO_2 and the reverse reaction are slow, and in biological systems are catalyzed by the zinc-containing enzyme carbonic anhydrase.

SiO_2 and especially GeO_2 are less soluble in water than is CO_2, although solubility of SiO_2 increases at a high temperatures and pressures. **Silicic acid** is a complex mixture of polymeric forms and only under very dilute conditions is the monomer $Si(OH)_4$ formed. SiO_2 reacts with aqueous HF to give $[SiF_6]^{2-}$.

The structural chemistry of carbonates, silicates and germinates shows parallels with the different oxide structures. All **carbonates** (*e.g.*, $CaCO_3$) have discrete planar CO_3^{2-} anions (see Topic C1, structure 11). **Silicate** structures are based on tetrahedral SiO_4 groups, which can be isolated units as in Mg_2SiO_4, but often polymerize by Si–O–Si corner-sharing links to give rings, chains, sheets and 3D frameworks. Many germinates are structurally similar to silicates, but germanium more readily adopts six-coordinate structures.

Other Compounds

Carbon disulfide CS_2 has similar bonding to CO_2, but SiS_2 differs from silica in having a chain structure based on edge-sharing tetrahedra, and GeS_2 adopts the CDI_2 layer structure with octahedral Ge.

Nitrogen compounds include the toxic species cyanogens $(CN)_2$ (2) and the **cyanide ion** CN^-, which forms strong complexes with many transition metals. Si_3N_4 and Si_2N_2O are polymeric compounds with single Si–N bonds, both forming refractory, hard and chemically resistant solids of interest in engineering applications.

$$N \equiv C - C \equiv N$$
2

Compounds with metals show a great diversity. A few carbides and silicides of electropositive metals, such as Al_3C_4 and Ca_2Si, could be formulated with C^{4-} and Si^{4-} ions although the bonding is certainly not very ionic. Compounds with transition metals are metallic in character, those of Si and Ge being normally regarded as **intermetallic compounds,** those of carbon as **interstitial compounds** with small carbon atoms occupying holes in the metal lattice. Some such as TaC and WC are remarkably hard, high melting and chemically unreactive, and are used in cutting tools. Fe_3C occurs in steel and contributes to the mechanical hardness.

Many compounds with E–E bonding are known. CaC_2 has C_2^{2-} ions (isoelectronic with N_2) and reacts with water to give ethyne C_2H_2. On the other hand, KSi and $CaSi_2$ are **Zinti compounds** with single-bonded structures. Ge (like Sn and Pb) forms some polyanions such as $[Ge_9]^{4-}$.

Organometallic compounds containing metal-carbon bonds are formed by nearly all metals, and are discussed under the relevant elements. Some analogous Si and Ge compounds are known.

6.5 Nitrogen

Nitrogen occurs in nature where it constitute nearly three fifth of the earth's atmosphere. It also occurs in the combined form as nitrates. Nitrogen is an essential element for living matter because it is an important constituent of proteins and even human body. Phosphorus is also essential for life because its compound control almost all biological processes.

Dinitrogen makes up 79 mol % of dry air. The element is essential for life and is one of the elements often in short supply, as fixation of atmospheric nitrogen to form chemically usable compounds is a difficult process.

Nitrogen is obtained from the atmosphere by liquefaction and fractional distillation. Its normal boiling point (77 K or –196°C) and its ready availability make it a useful coolant. It reacts directly with rather few elements and is often used as an inert filling or 'blanket' for metallurgical processes. The majority of industrial nitrogen, however is used to make ammonia and further compounds.

Nitrogen is moderately electronegative element but the great strength of the triple bond makes N_2 kinetically and thermodynamically stable. The atom can form three single bonds, generally with a pyramidal geometry (see Topics C1 and C2), but also has a notable tendency to multiple bonding. Its unusually rich redox chemistry is illustrated in the Frost diagram.

Ammonia (NH₃)

Ammonia is manufactured in larger molar quantities than any other substance. The two important sources for the manufacture of ammonia are:.ammoniacal liquor and air. The latter is really a source of nitrogen which is converted into ammonia either by IIaber's synthetic process or by the Cynamide process.

(i) **From Ammoniacal Liquor.** Coal gas manufactured by the destructive distillation of coal is cooled and bubbled through water where ammonium salts accompanying coal gas are dissolved. The concentrated solution of ammonium salts so obtained is called *ammoniacal liquor*. Milk of lime is added to the ammoniacal liquor and steam blown through the mixture. The mixture of steam and ammonia evolved is bubbled through sulphuric acid. Ammonium sulphate thus formed is crystallized out. It is largely used as a fertilizer.

$$2NH_3 + H_2SO_4 \longrightarrow (NH_4)_2SO_4$$

To get liquour ammonia. Ammonia evolved is bubbled through water under pressure when concentrated solution of ammonia is obtained.

(ii) **By Haber's Process.** Large quantities of ammonia are manufactured by direct union of the elements by the *Haber's Process.*

Theory. Nitrogen and hydrogen combine according to the equation,

$$N_2 + 3H_2 = 2NH_3; \qquad \Delta H = -93.6 \text{ kJ}$$

The reaction is reversible, exothermic and proceeds with a decrease in volume. According to Le Chatelier principle, favourable conditions **for maximum yield of ammonia are:**

(a) *Low temperature.* Optimum temperature for the reaction has been experimentally found to be 720-770 K.

(b) *High pressure* of the order of 200-900 atmospheres.

(c) *Catalyst.* It may be finely divided ion with molybdenum or calcium as promoter or finely divided osmium or uranium or finely divided nickel deposited over *pumice stone* or ferric oxide with traces of silica and potassium oxide.

(iii) **By Cynamide Process.** Hydrolysis of calcium cyanamide with super heated steam at 450 K is another important factor for the manufacture of ammonia.

Ammonia is used in the manufacture of nitric acid (by **octwalds process**). It is also used in the manufacture of plastics and pharmaceuticals.

It is a good **Lewis base**. It acts as a monodeutate bigand and forms complexes. In water it acts as a **Bronsted base**.

$$NH_3 + H_2O \rightleftharpoons NH_4^+ + OH^- \quad ; \quad K_b = 1.8 \times 10^{-8}$$
base   acid   acid   base

NH_4^+ forms salts. The structure of salts because NH_4^+ can sometimes undergo *hydrogen bonding e.g.,* NH_4^+ has *tetrahedral wurtzite structure* and not a rocksalt like structure of KF (though both K^+ and NH_4^+ have similar radius). The tetrahedral coordination is ideal for the formation of hydrogen bonds between NH_4^+ and F^- ions. When heated ammonium salts (NH_4^+) generally dissociate.

$$NH_4Cl(s) \rightleftharpoons NH_3 (g) + HCl (g)$$

Ammonia has a normal bonding point of –33°C. As with water, this value is much higher than expected from the normal group trend, a manifestation of strong hydrogen bonding. Liquid ammonia also undergoes autoprolysis although to a lesser extent than water. It is a good solvent for many ionic substances, and is much more basic than water. Ammonium salts act as acids and amides as bases. Ammonia is kinetically inert under strongly reducing conditions and will dissolve alkali metals to give solutions with free solvated electrons present.

Oxidation States

Nitrogen shows a number of oxidation as states such as –3, 0, +1, +3, +5 etc. various oxidation states are shown diagrammatically.

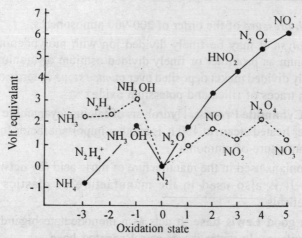

Fig. 6.2. Frost diagram showing the redox states of nitrogen in water at pH = 0 (continuous line) and pH = 14 (dashed line).

Hydrazine N_2H_4 **(1)** can be made by the Rauschig synthesis:

$$H-\ddot{\overset{|}{\underset{|}{N}}}-\overset{|}{\underset{H}{N}}-H$$

1

$$2NH_3 + NaOCl \rightarrow N_2H_4 + NaCl + H_2O$$

Its combustion to give N_2 and H_2O is extremely exothermic ($\Delta H = -620$ kJ mol^{-1}) and it has been used as a rocket fuel. The explosive hydrogen azide HN_3 is the conjugate acid of the azide ion N_3^- **(2)**. Another hydrogen compound is hydroxylamine NH_2OH.

$$\overset{-}{N} = \overset{+}{N} = \overset{-}{N}$$

2

Nitrogen forms an enormous variety of organic compounds. **Amines** like methylamine CH_3NH_2 and trimethylamine $(CH_3)_3N$ can be considered as derived from ammonia by replacing one or more H atoms with alkyl or aryl groups. Like ammonia, amines are basic and form complexes with transition metals. **Tetraalkyl ammonium ions** like $[(C_4H_9)_4N]^+$ are useful when large anions are needed in inorganic synthesis. Nitrogen also forms **heterocyclic compounds** like pyridine C_5H_5N.

Oxides and Oxyacids of Nitrogen

The five known oxides and nitrogen are:

(i)   Nitrous oxide or **Laughing gas,** N_2O.

(ii) Nitric acid or nitrous fumes, NO

(iii) Nitrogen trioxide, N_2O_3. It is also called nitrous anhydride.

(iv) Dinitrogen tetroxide, N_2O_4. It is mixed anhydride of nitrous (HNO_2) and nitric acid (HNO_3).

(v)   Nitrogen pentroxide, N_2O_5. It is nitric anhydride.

Preparation and Properties of Oxides of Nitrogen

Nitrous oxide N_2O can be made by heating ammonium nitrate. It is isoelectronic with CO_2 and somewhat unreactive, and is used as an anaesthetic ('laughing gas') and as a propellant for aerosols. **Nitric oxide** NO and **nitrogen dioxide** NO_2 are the normal products of reaction of oxygen and nitrogen at high temperatures, or of the oxidation of ammonia. They are both odd-electron molecules. NO_2 dimerizes reversibly at low temperatures to make N_2O_4, but NO has very little tendency to dimerize in the gas phase, probably because the odd electron is delocalized in a π antibonding orbital (see Topic C4; the molecular orbital diagram is like that for CO but with one more electron). NO reacts with oxygen to give NO_2. it can act as a ligand in transition metal complexes. The other oxides of nitrogen are less stable; N_2O_3 is shown in *Fig.* below; N_2O_5 is normally found as $[NO_2]^+[NO_3]^-$; and NO_3 is an unstable radical that (like NO and NO_2) plays a role in atmospheric chemistry.

NO^+ and NO_2^+ (isoelectronic with CO and CO_2, respectively) can be formed by the action of strong oxidizing agents on NO or NO_2 in acid solvents such as H_2SO_4, and are known as solid salts (*e.g.,* $NO^+[AsF_6]^-$). The **nitrite** and **nitrate** ions NO_2^- and NO_3^- are formed respectively from bitrous acid HNO_2 and nitric acid HNO_3. As expected from Pauling's rules, HNO_2 is a weak acid in water and HNO_3 a strong acid. Metal nitrates and nitrites are strong oxidizing agents, generally very soluble in water. Other less stable oxoacids are known, mostly containing N–N bonds. Although the free acid corresponding to phosphoric acid H_5PO_4 is unknown, it is possible to make **orthonitrates** containing the tetrahedral NO_4^{3-} ion. Nitric acid is a major industrial chemical made from ammonia by catalytic oxidation to NO_2, followed by reaction with water and more oxygen:

$$2NO_2 + H_2O + 1/2 \ O_2 \rightarrow 2HNO_3$$

It is used to make NH_4NO_3 fertilizer, and in many industrial processes.

The redox chemistry of nitrogen compounds in aqueous solution is illustrated in the Frost diagram. All oxides and oxoacids are strong oxidizing agents, and all oxidation states except –3, 0 and +5 are susceptible to disproportionation. The detailed reactions are, however, mostly controlled by kinetic rather than the oxodynamic consideration. In conjunction with oxidizable groups, as in ammonium nitrate NH_4NO_3 or in organic nitro compounds, N–O compounds can be powerful explosives.

Structures of N_2O, NO, N_2O_3, N_2O_4, NO^+, NO_2^-, NO_3^-

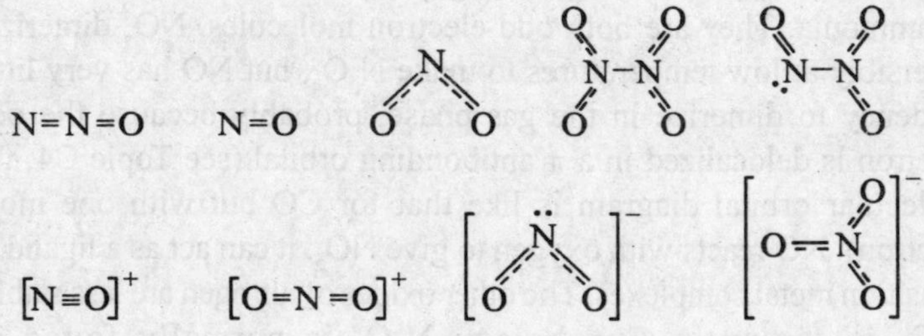

Fig. 6.3. Structures of some oxides, oxocations and oxoanions of nitrogen.

Other Compounds

Compounds with sulfur are called fluorides. Apart from its fluorides, nitrogen **halides** are thermodynamically unstable and very explosive. The trifluoride NF_3 can be prepared by direct reaction of NH_3 and F_2. It is kinetically inert and nontoxic. Further fluorination gives the N^V species NF_4^+.

$$NF_3 + 2F_2 + SbF_3 \rightarrow [NF_4]^+[SbF_6]^-$$

The *oxofluoride* ONF_3 is also known. Like NF_4^+ it is isoelectronic with NO_4^{3-} and must be described by a similar valence structure (3). N_2F_4 is interesting in that like N_2O_4 it readily dissociates into NF_2 radicals. Double-bonded N_2F_2 exists in *cis* (4) and *trans* (5) forms, the former being thermodynamically more stable.

Nitrogen reacts directly with some electropositive metals to form **nitrides** such as Li_3N and Ca_3N_2. Although these can be formulated with nitride ion N^{3-} the bonding may be partially covalent. Other compounds with metals are **amides** and **imides** (containing NH_2^- and NH^{2-}, respectively) and **azides** containing N_3^-. Metal azides are thermodynamically unstable and often explosive.

6.6 Phosphorus, Arsenic and Antimony

Phosphorus occurs as phosphates such as the 3 $Ca_3(PO_4)_2$. CaF_2 (the ore is called **apatite**).

Reactivity. Nitrogen is present as N_2 ($N \equiv N$) and is very inert at ordinary temperatures and does not react with many metals directly. However at higher temperatures it reacts with *s* block elements. For example it forms magnesium and lithium nitrides when they are heated in it.

$$3Mg \ (s) + N_2 \ (g) \rightarrow Mg_3N_2 \ (s)$$
$$6 \ Li \ (s) + N_2 \ (g) \rightarrow 2 \ Li_3 \ N \ (s)$$

Phosphorous, although less electronegative than nitrogen, combines more readily with metals to form phosphides since it is more reactive than nitrogen.

Arsenic and Antimony are much more rarer. They occur in minerals such as **realgar**. As_4S_4 and stibnite Sb_2S_3, but are mostly obtained as byproducts from the processing of sulfide ores of other elements. Elemental P is obtained by reduction of calcium phosphate.

The complex reaction approximates to:

$$2Ca_3(PO_4)_2 + 6SiO_2 + 10C \rightarrow 6CaSiO_3 + 10CO + P_4$$

Most allotropes phosphates are used more directly without conversion to the element.

Phosphorus has many allotropes. It is most commonly encountered as **white phosphorous,** which contains tetrahedral P_4 molecules (1). Other forms, that are quite stable thermodynamically but kinetically harder to make, contain polymeric networks with three-coordinate P. White phosphorous is highly reactive and toxic. It will combine directly with most elements, glows in air at room temperature as a result of slow oxidation, and combusts spontaneously at a temperature above 35°C. Arsenic can also form As_4 molecules, but the common solid forms of this element and Sb are polymeric with three-coordination. They are markedly less reactive than phosphorous.

1

Uses

Large quantities of phosphates are used, in fertilizers, food products, detergents and other household products. For fertilizer applications apatite is converted by the action of acid to the much more soluble compound $Ca(H_2PO_4)_2$, known as 'superphosphate'.

Hydrides and Organic Derivatives

The hydrides **phosphine** PH_3, **arsine** As_sH_3 and **stibine** SbH_3 can be prepared by hydrolysis of metal phosphates, or by reduction of molecular compounds like PCl_3. They are very toxic gases, with decreasing thermal stability P > As > Sb. Unlike ammonia they are not basic in water. The hydrazine analog diphosphane P_2H_4 and a few other catenated compounds with P–P bonds can be made, although their stability is low.

Organic derivatives include alkyl and aryl phosphines such as triphenyl phosphine $(C_6H_5)_3P$. As with the hydrides these compounds are much less basic than the corresponding nitrogen compounds towards acceptors such as H$^+$, but are good ligand for transition metals in low oxidation states, as they have π-acceptor properties (see Topic H9). Cyclic polyarsanes such as (AsPh)$_6$ (where Ph is a phenyl group, C$_2$H$_5$) with As–As bonds are readily made, and with very bulky organic groups it is possible to prepare compounds with E = E double bonds, for example,

$$2((CH_3)_3Si)_3CAsCl_2 + 2Li(C_4H_9) \rightarrow ((CH_3)_3Si)_3CAs=AsC((CH_3)_3Si)_3 + 2LiCl + 2C_4H_9Cl$$

Unlike with nitrogen, the five-coordinate compounds Ph$_5$E are known. The P and As compounds have the normal trigonal bipyramidal geometry but Ph$_5$Sb is unexpectedly square pyramidal (**2**).

$$
\begin{array}{c}
Ph \\
| \\
Ph \diagdown \; Sb \text{-\,-} Ph \\
Ph \diagup \quad \diagdown Ph \\
Ph
\end{array}
$$

2

Halides

Phosphorous forms the binary compounds P$_2$X$_4$ (with a P–P bond), PX$_3$ and PX$_4$ with all halogens. With As and Sb a complete set of EX$_3$ compounds is known, but the only E^V halides stable under normal conditions are AsF$_5$, SbF$_5$ and SbCl$_5$. AsCl$_5$ has been identified from the UV irradiation of PCl$_3$ in liquid Cl$_2$ but decomposes above – 50ºC. Most known halides can be obtained by direct reaction of the elements in appropriate proportions, but P and F together form only PF$_5$ and the trihalide can be prepared by reacting PCl, with Znf$_2$ or Hgf$_2$. The molecular substances have the expected structures, pyramidal for EX$_3$ and trigonal bipyramidal for EX$_5$ (see Topic C2). However, some have a marked tendency to undergo halide transfer, and in the solid state PCl$_5$ and PBr$_5$ form the ionic structures [PCl$_4$]$^+$ [PCl$_6$]$^-$ and [PBr$_4$]$^+$ Br$^-$, respectively. Presumably it is the lattice energy associated with an ionic solid that stabilizes these forms. Many halide complexes are known. AsF$_5$ and SbF$_5$ are Lewis acids with a very strong affinity for F, giving $[AsF_6]^-$ or fluoride-bridged species such as $[Sb_2F_{11}]^-$ (3).

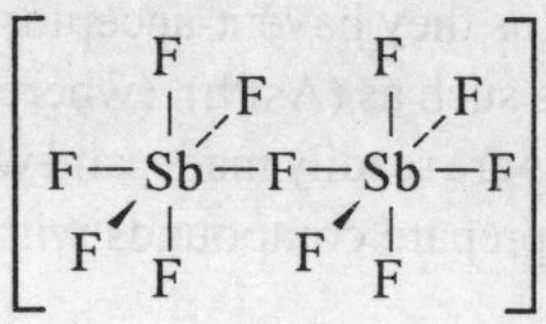

$$\left[\begin{array}{c} F \quad\quad F \\ | \quad F \quad\quad | \quad F \\ F-Sb-F-Sb-F \\ F \quad | \quad\quad F \quad | \\ \quad F \quad\quad\quad F \end{array} \right]^-$$

3

Oxohalides EOX_3 form tetrahedral molecules with E = P, but polymeric structures with As and Sb. $POCl_3$ is an important intermediate in the manufacture of organophosphorous compounds, used, for example, as insecticides.

Oxides and Oxoacids

P_4O_6 (4) and P_4O_{10} (5) can be obtained by direct reaction of the elements, the P^V compound 'phosphorous pentoxide' being the normal product when phosphorous burns in air. Under carefully controlled conditions immediate oxides P_4O_n (n = 7, 8, 9) can be made. The oxides of As and Sb have polymeric structures, and include a mixed valency compound Sb_2O_4 with Sb^{III} in pyramidal coordination and octahedral Sb^V.

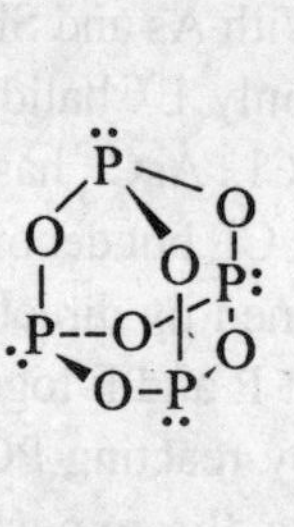

4 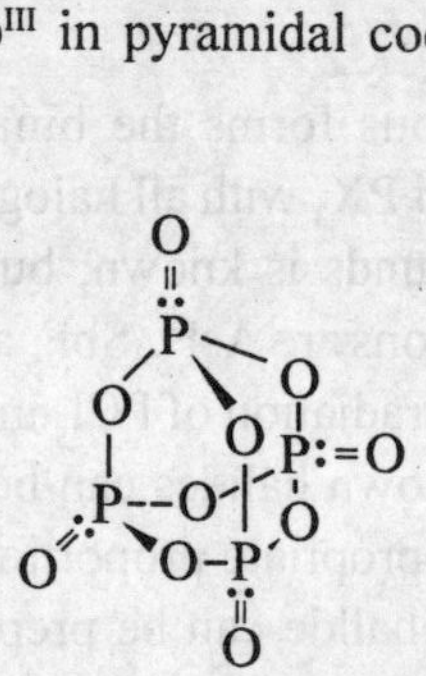   **5**

P_4O_{10} is a very powerful dehydrating agent. It reacts with water to form **phosphoric acid** H_3PO_4. This is a weak tribasic acid with successive acidity constants exemplifying Pauling's rules $pK_1 = 2.15$, $pK_2 = 7.20$ and $pK_3 = 12.37$. Neutral solutions contain about equal concentrations of $H_2PO_4^-$ and HPO_4^{2-} and are widely used as buffers. A wide variety of metal **orthophosphates,** containing ions with each possible stage of deprotonation, are known. Further addition of P_4O_{10} to concentrated phosphoric acid results in the formation **polyphosphates** with P–O–P linkages as in silicates. These linkages are kinetically stable in aqueous solution and are important in biology. **Metaphosphates** such as KPO_3 have infinite chains of corner-sharing octahedra as in the isoelectronic metasilictaes such as $CaSiO_3$.

The P^{III} oxoacids **phosphorous acid** H_3PO_3 does not have the structure $P(OH)_3$ that its formula suggests, but is tetrahedral with a PH bond: $HPO(OH)_2$. It is thus diprotic with a similar pK_1 to phosphoric acid. The trend is continued with hypophosphorous acid $H_2PO(OH)$. Both acids are strong reducing agents.

Arsenic acid H_3AsO_4 is similar to phosphoric acid but is a relatively strong oxidizing agent. Sb^V oxo compounds have different structures and are based on the octahedral $[Sb(OH)_6]^-$ ion. Aqueous As^{III} and Sb^{III} species are hard to characterize, they are much more weakly acidic than phosphorous acid and are probably derived from $As(OH)_3$ and $Sb(OH)_3$. The corresponding salts tend to have polymeric structures, for example, $NaAsO_2$ with oxygen linked $[-As(O^-)-O]$ chains isoelectronic with SeO_2.

Other Compounds

The sulfides of As and Sb are found in nature. As_2S_3 and Sb_2S_3 with the stoichiometries expected for As^{III} and Sb^{III} have polymeric structures. Compounds such as As_6S_4 (**6**) and $P_4S\pi$ ($n = 3$–10) are molecules based on P_4 or As_4 tetrahedra with bridging –S– groups inserted; some of the phosphorus compounds also have termical P = S groups similar to P = O in **5**.

6

Phosphazines are compounds containing repeated $-PX_2N-$ units. For example, the reaction

$$nPCl_5 + nNH_4Cl \rightarrow (NPCl_2)_n + 4nHCl$$

gives rings and chains with a distribution of n values. The (PX_2N) unit has the same number of valence electrons as (Me_2SiO), which forms silicone polymers. In the valence structure as drawn in 7 P and N carry formal charges, but there is probably some $P = N$ double bonding.

7

Binary compounds with metals are generally of low ionic character. Many those with transition metals have the NiAs and related structures and show metallic properties. Some compounds appear to contain polyanionic species (*e.g.,* P_2^{4-} isoelectronic with S_2^{2-} in Sr_2P_2, and P_7^{3-} in Na_3P_7), although the bonding is certainly not fully ionic.

6.7 Oxygen

It occurs in nature in the *nature state* (as a constituent of atmospheric air). The upper atmosphere contains a certain amount of oxygen in atomic form which is formed due to the action of *u.v.light*.

$$\underset{\text{(air)}}{O_2} + Hv \longrightarrow \underset{\substack{\text{atomic} \\ \text{oxygen}}}{O(g) + O(g)}$$

These free oxygen atoms combine with molecular-oxygen (O_2) to form Ozone (O_3) which may be considered as an oxide of oxygen.

$$O_2(g) + O(g) \longrightarrow \underset{\text{(ozone)}}{O_3(g)}$$

It also occurs in *combined form* in water (H_2O) earthen crust, plants and animal tissues. It also occurs as phosphates, carbonates, nitrates, oxides, sulphates etc.

Oxygen can be extracted from the atmosphere by liquefaction and fractional distillation. The liquid boils at $-183°C$ (90 K) and is dangerous when mixed with combustible materials. The compressed ags is used in metallurgy (*e.g.*, steel-making) and the liquid as an oxidizer for rocket propulsion.

Oxygen has two allotropes, the normal dioxygen O_2 **form** and **ozone O_3 (1)** formed by subjecting O_2 to an electric discharge. Ozone is a trace constituent of the atmosphere, where it plays an important role as an absorber of UV radiation.

1

As predicted by molecular orbital theory dioxygen has two unpaired electrons and some of its chemistry shows diradical characteristics in particular, it reacts readily with other radicals. **Singlet oxygen** is an excited state in which the two electrons in the π antibonding orbitals have paired spins. It produced in some chemical reactions and has different chemical reactivity.

Oxygen is the second most electronegative element after fluorine, and forms thermodynamically stable compounds with nearly all elements. It rivals fluorine in the ability to stabilize the highest known oxidation states of many elements, examples where there is no corresponding fluoride being $Cl^{VII}O_4^-$ and $Os^{VIII}O_4$. Oxidation reactions with O_2 are often show because of the strength of the O = O double bond (490 kJ mol^{-1}).

Oxides

Oxygen forms binary compounds with nearly all elements. Most may be prepared by direct reaction, although other methods (such as the thermal decomposition at carbonates or hydroxides) are sometimes more convenient. Oxides may be broadly classified as **molecular,**

polymeric or **ionic**. But Covalent oxides are formed with nonmetals and may contain terminal ($E = O$) or bridging ($E-O-E$) oxygen. Especially strong double bonds are formed with Al and S. Bridging is more common with heavier elements and leads to the formation of many polymeric structures such as SiO_2.

Water H_2O is the most abundant molecular substance on Earth. It is highly polar compound. Its physical properties are dominated by hydrogen bonding. It is an excellent solvent for ionic substances and reactions. Various **hydrated salts** are known (*e.g.*, $CuSO_4.5H_2O$), which contain water bound by coordination to metal ions and/or hydrogen bonding to anions. Autoprotolysis gives the ions H_3O^+ and OH^-, which are also known in solid salts, H_3O^+ with anions or strong acids (e.g., $[H_3O]^+[NO_3]^-$; hydrated species such as $[H_5O_2]^+$ are also known), and OH^- in **hydroxides**, which are formed by many metals.

Oxides of most metallic elements have structures that may be broadly classified as ionic. The closed-shell O^{2-} ion is unknown in the gas phase, the reaction

$$O^-(g) + e^- \longrightarrow O^{2-}(g)$$

being very endothermic. It is therefore only the large lattice energy obtained with the O^{2-} ion that stabilizes it in solids. The variety of coordination numbers (CN) of oxide is large, examples being:

CN =	2	3	4	6	8
	ReO_3	TiO_2	ZnO	MgO	Li_2O

Oxide has a notable tendency for symmetrical coordination in ionic solids (linear planar or tetrahedral with CN = 2, 3 or 4, respectively) and unlike sulfide rarely forms layer structures.

The distinction between ionic and polymeric solids is not absolute, and oxides of metals with low electropositive character (e.g., HgO) or in high oxidation states (e.g., CrO_3) are better described as having polar covalent bonds. A few metals in very high oxidation states form molecular oxides (*e.g.*, Mn_2O_7, OsO_4).

Many ternary and more complex oxides are known. It is normal to distinguish **complex oxides** such as $CaCO_3$, which contain discrete oxoanions, and mixed **oxides** such as $CaTiO_3$, which do not.

In water, the very basic O^{2-} ion reacts to form hydroxide:

$$O^{2-} (aq) + H_2O \longrightarrow 2OH^- (aq)$$

Table 6.2. Some oxoacids, showing their anhydrides and the anions formed by them

Anhydride	Acid name	Acid formula	Anion formula
B_2O_3	Boric	$B(OH)_3$	$[B(OH)_4]^{-a}$
CO_2	Carbonic	H_2CO_3	CO_3^{2-b}
SiO_2	Silicic	$Si(OH)_4$	$SiOH_4^{4-a, b}$
N_2O_3	Nitrous	HNO_2	NO_2^-
N_2O_8	Nitric	HNO_3	NO_3^-
P_4O_{10}	Phosphoric	H_3PO_4	PO_4^{3-b}
SO_2	Sulfurous	H_2SO_3	SO_3^{2-b}
SO_3	Sulfuric	H_2SO_4	SO_3^{2-b}
Cl_2O	Hypochiorous	$ClOH$	ClO^-
$(Cl_2O_5)^c$	Chioric	$HClO_3$	ClO_3^-
Cl_2O_7	Perchioric	$HClO_4$	ClO_4^-

[a]Anion with a strong tendency to polymerize and form complex structures.
[b]Polyprotic acid with intermediate states of ionization possible.
[c]Parent anhydride unknown.

and so ionic oxides are **basic** and either form alkaline solutions if soluble in water, or otherwise dissolve in acid solution. Covalent oxides (including those such as CrO_3 formed by metals in high oxidation states) **are acidic** and react with water to form **oxoacids**:

$$P_4O_{10} + 6H_2O \rightarrow 4H_3PO_4 \rightleftharpoons 4H_2PO_4^- + 4H^+ \rightleftharpoons \text{etc.}$$

Such oxides may therefore be considered as **acid anhydrides**. *Table* above shows a selection of oxoacids with their anhydrides and illustrates the conventional nomenclature. For example, **sulfurous** and **sulfuric** acids are display the lower (+4) and higher (+6) oxidation state, respectively, and their anions are called **sulfite** and **sulfate**.

Some oxides are **atmospheric** and have both acidic and basic properties; this often happens with a metal ion with a higher charge/size ratio such as Be^{2+} or Al^{3+}. A few nonmetallic oxides (*e.g.*, CO) are **neutral** and have no appreciable acid or basic properties.

Peroxides and Superoxides

Adding one or two electrons to dioxygen gives the **superoxide** O_2^- and **peroxide** O_2^{2-} ions. As the added electrons occupy the π antibonding orbital, the bond becomes progressively weaker and longer. Supeoxides MO_2, rather than simple oxides M_2O are the normal products of reacting the heavier alkali metals with oxygen; peroxides M_2O_2 are also formed. This can be explained by lattice energy arguments. With most metal ions, the higher lattice energy obtained with O^{2-} forces the disproportionation of the larger O_2^- and O_2^{2-} ions. With large, low-charged cations, however, the lattice energy gain is insufficient to cause disproportionation. The peroxide ion can also be stabilized in **peroxo** complexes, where it acts as a ligand to transition metals, as in $[Cr^V(O_2)_4]^{3-}$.

The simplest covalent peroxide is **hydrogen peroxide** H_2O_2, which is normally encountered in aqueous solution. Although kinetically fairly stable, it can act as either an oxidizing agent (giving H_2O) or a reducing agent (giving O_2), and many transition metal ions catalyze its decomposition. Organic peroxides (R_2O_2) and peroxoacids (*e.g.*, the percarbonate ion, **2**) contain the fairly weak peroxo O–O linkage. Some covalent peroxides can be unpredictably and dangerously explosive.

$$\left[\begin{array}{c} O \\ \parallel \\ O-C \\ \diagup \quad \diagdown \\ O \qquad O \end{array} \right]^{2-}$$

2

Positive Oxidation States

Reaction with strong oxidizing agents gives the O_2^+ ion, which has a stronger and shorter bond than O_2.

$$O_2 + BF_3 + 1/2\ F_2 \rightarrow [O_2^+][BF_4]^-$$

Fluorides include F_2O and F_2O_2. The latter has a considerably shorter O–O bond than in peroxides fact that may indicate some contribution of ionic valence structures such as (**3**), which allow a degree of multiple bonding. All compounds in positive oxidation states are very strongly oxidizing. Compounds with heavier halogens are normally regarded as halogen oxides.

$$F^- \quad O = \overset{+}{O} \diagdown F$$

3

6.8 Sulphur, Selenium and Tellurium

Sulphur occurs in *native state*. It is widely distributed in native constituting about 0.1% of **earth's crust**. It occurs in combined state worstly as **sulphides** and **sulphates** of metals. The biggest sulphur deposits of the world are in Louisiana and Texas (U.S.A).

These elements (S, Se, Te) are collectively known as **chalcogens**.

Many less electropositive metals known as **chalcophiles** are found commonly as sulfide minerals; some important examples are pyrites (FeS_2), sphalerite (zinc blende, ZnS), molybdenite (MoS_2), cinnabar (HgS) and galena (PbS). Volatile sulfur compounds such as H_2S and organic compounds are also found in petroleum and natural gas. The element is used in large amounts for the manufacture of **sulfuric acid** (see below). Selenium and tellurium are much rarer, found as minor components of sulfide minerals.

Allotropes

Sulfur has several allotropic forms, the most stable of which are molecular solids containing S_8 rings. The elemental forms of Se and Te have spiral chains and are semiconductors. In all of these solids each atom forms two single bonds to neighbours. Sulfur combines directly with oxygen and halogens (except I), and with many less electronegative elements to form sulfides. The other elements show similar properties although reactivity declines down the group.

Chalcogenides

Molecular compounds include H_2S and its analogs, and many organic compounds. The hydrides are made by the action of Bronsted acids on metal chalcogenides. They are extremely toxic gases, weakly acidic in water (*e.g.,* for H_2S, $pK_1 = 6.8$, $pK_2 = 14.2$). Many polysulfanes H_2S_n containing S–S bonds are also known.

Solid **chalcogenides** are formed by all metallic elements and by many non-metals. Only with the most electropositive metals do they commonly have the same structures as oxides. With transition metals, compounds MX (which are frequently of variable stoichiometry) have the nickel arsenide or similar structures in which metal-metal bonding is present. MX_2 compounds either has layer structure (*e.g.,* TiS_2, $TiSe_2$, $TiTe_2$) all CdI_2 type or structures containing diatomic ions (*e.g.,* FeS_2 has S_2 units and so is formally a compound of FE^{II} not Fe^{IV}). Chalcogenides of electropositive metals are decomposed by water giving hydrides such as H_2S, but those of less electropositive elements (often the ones forming sulfide ores, see above) are insoluble in water.

Halides

A selection of the most important halides is show in *Table* below. With sulfur the fluorides are most stable and numerous, but Se and Te show an increasing range of heavier halides. Compounds such as S_2Cl_2 and S_2F_{10} have S–S bonds; S_2F_2 has another isomer $S = SF_2$. Sulfur halides are molecular and monomeric with structures expected from VSEPR (*e.g.,* SF_4 'see=saw', SF_6 octahedral). With the heavier elements increasing polymerization is found, as in $(TeCl_4)_4$ **(1)** and related tetramers.

1

The hexahalides are kinetically inert, but most other halides are highly reactive and are hydrolized in water giving oxides and oxoacids. Intermediate hydrolysis products are **oxohalides** of which **thionyl chloride** $SOCl_2$ and **sulfuryl chloride** SO_2Cl_2 are industrially important compounds.

Some of the halides show donor and/or acceptor properties. For example, SF_4 reacts with both Lewis acids (forming compounds such as $[SF_3]^+[BF_4]^-$) and bases (forming either simple adducts such as $C_5H_5N:SF_4$ with pyridine, or compounds containing the square pyramidal ion $[SF_5]^-$). The complex ions $[SeX_6]^{2-}$ and $[TeX_6]^{2-}$ (X = Cl, Br, I) are interesting as they appear to have regular octahedral structures in spite of the presence of a nonbonding electron pair on the central atom.

Table 6.3. Principal halides of S, Se and Te.

S	Se	Te
S_2F_2, SF_2, S_2F_4, SF_4, S_2F_{10}, SF_6	SeF_4, SeF_6	TeF_4, TeF_6
S_2Cl_2, SCl_2	Se_2Cl_2, $(SeCl_4)_4$	Te_2Cl, $(TeCl_4)_4$
$S\pi Br_2$	Se_2Br_2, $(SeBr_4)_4$	Te_2Br, $(TeBr_4)_4$
		Te_2I, Te_4I_4, $(TeI_4)_4$

Oxides and Oxoacids

The important oxides of all three elements (E) are EO_2 and EO_3. Sulfur in addition forms many oxides of low thermodynamic stability, for example S_nO with a structure containing an S_n ring. **Sulfur dioxide** SO_2 is the major product of burning sulfur and organic sulfur compounds in air, and is a serious air pollutant giving rise (after oxidation to H_2SO_4); to acid rain. With one lone-pair, SO_2 is a bent molecule and has both Lewis acid and basic properties. The liquid is a good solvent for reactions with strong oxidizing agents. SO_2 dissolves in water giving acid solutions containing the pyramidal hydrogensulfide (HSO_3) and **sulfite** (SO_3^{2-}) ions. The expected sulfurous acid H_2SO_3, however, is present only in very low concentrations. SeO_2 and TeO_2 have polymeric structures and give oxoacids salts similar to those from sulfur.

2

Sulfur trioxide SO_3 is obtained industrially as a route to sulfuric acid, by oxidizing SO_2 with oxygen using a vanadium oxide catalyst. It can exist as a monomeric planar molecule but readily gives cyclic S_3O_9 trimers and linear polymers with corner-sharing SO_4 units. The highly exothermic reaction with water gives **sulfuric acid** H_2SO_4, which is the world's major industrial chemical, being used in many large-scale processes for making fertilizers, dyestuffs, soaps and detergents, and synthetic fibers. Anhydrous sulfuric acid undergoes a series of acid-base equilibria like

$$2H_2SO_4 \rightleftharpoons H_3SO_4^- + HSO_4^-$$

$$2H_2SO_4 \rightleftharpoons H_3O^+ + HS_2O_7^-$$

it is a very strongly acid medium, in which HNO_3 (a strong acid in water) acts as a base

$$HNO_3 + 2H_2SO_4 \rightarrow NO_2^+ + H_3O^+ + 2HSO_4^-$$

The resulting 'nitrating mixture' is used for preparing aromatic nitro compounds by electophillic reactions of NO_2^+.

Reaction of HF with SO_3 gives **fluorosulfonic acid** HSO_3F, which is even more strongly acidic than sulfuric acid. In mixtures with SO_3 and powerful fluoride acceptors such as SbF_5 it gives **superacid media,** which are capable of protonating even most organic compounds.

SeO_3 and selenic acid H_2SeO_4 are similar to the sulfur analogs except that they are more strongly oxidizing. Tellurium behaves differently, as telluric acid has the octahedral $Te(OH)_6$ structure, which, as expected from Pauling's rules, is a very weak acid.

There are many other oxoacids of sulfur, of which the most important are peroxodisulfate $S_2O_8^{2-}$, which has a peroxo (O–O) bond, and compounds with S–S bonds including thiosulfatae $S_2O_3^{2-}$, dithionite $S_2O_4^{2-}$ and tetrathionate $S_4O_6^{2-}$. The reaction

$$2S_2O_3^{2-} + I_2 \rightarrow 2I^- + S_4O_6^{2-}$$

is used for the quantitative estimation of I_2 in aqueous solution.

Other Compounds

Oxidation of the elements (e.g., by AsF_5) in suitable solvent such as SO_2 or H_2SO_4 gives a series of **polyatomic cations** such as $[S_8]^{2+}$ and $[S_4]^{2-}$. The latter (and its Se and Te analogs) has a square-planar structure and can be regarded as a 6π-electron ring (see Topic C6).

Also of note are **sulfur-nitrogen compounds**. The cage-like S_4N_4 (see Topic C6) is formed by the reaction of S_2CL_2 with ammonia or NH_4Cl. Passing the heated vapour over silver wool gives the planar S_2N_2 with the same valence electron count as $[S_4]^{2+}$. Polymerization forms polythiazyl (SN), a linear polymer with metallic conductivity arising from delocalization of the one odd electron per SN unit.

6.9 Halogens

The name halogen, for fluorine, chlorine, bromine, iodine and astatine, the group 17 elements, has been derived from Greek meaning salt former-because all of them combine readily with metals to form salts. These elements comprise the most reactive group of non-metals. As is evident from their electronic configuration, (Table) all of them have seven electrons in their outermost orbit and have a tendency to gain one electron to yield the corresponding halide anions with noble gas configuration (eight electrons in the outermost orbit), *e.g.,*

$$Cl \quad + \quad e^- \quad \rightarrow \quad Cl^-$$

| One electron short of noble gas configuration | Noble gas configuration |

$$Br \quad + \quad e^- \quad \rightarrow \quad Br^-$$

Consequently all the halogens occur as halides. All these elements belong to the same group 17 of the periodic table which is indicated by the observed gradation in properties of these elements as is expected from their electronic configuration (Table).

All these elements do not occur free in nature and are always found in combination with metals, generally as the simple halides. The tendency to form anion, X^-, is weakest in astatine and is weak in iodine. Therefore, iodine occurs in nature as sodium iodate, $NaIO_3$. Fluorine occurs as cryolite, Na_2AlF_6 and fluorspar, CaF_2 whereas chlorine and bromine both occur as chlorides and bromides of sodium and potassium in sea water. Sea water contains roughly 3% of its weight as sodium and potassium halides. Astatine does not occur native and is a radioactive element obtained by bombardment of bismuth with α-particles. The following table gives the abundance of halogens in nature.

Table 6.4.   Relative abundance of halogens in nature

Elements	% by weight of earth's crust	Morality in sea water
Fluorine	0.08	10^{-4} M
Chlorine	0.19	0.56 M
Bromine	0.01	8×10^{-4} M
Iodine	10.4	
Astatine	negligible	Very small (negligible)

F and Cl are moderately abundant elements, principal sources being fluorite CaF_2 and halite NaCl, from which the very electronegative elements are obtained by electrolysis. Bromine is mainly obtained by oxidation of Br^- found in salt water; iodine occurs as iodates such as $Ca(IO_3)_2$. Astatine is radioactive and only minute amounts are found in nature. Chlorine is used (as ClO^- and ClO_2) in bleaches and is an important industrial chemical; other major uses (as with all the halogen) being in manufacture of halogenated organic compounds.

The elements form diatomic molecules, F_2 and Cl_2 being gases at normal temperature and pressure, Br_2 liquid and I_2 solid. They react directly with most other elements and are good oxidizing agents, although reactivity declines down the group. X–X bond strengths follow the sequence F < Cl > Br > I.

All the halogens readily form halide ions X⁻. Trends in chemistry resemble those found in other groups. Fluorine is limited to an octet of valence electrons. It is the most electronegative and reative of all elements and generally (as with oxygen) brings out the highest oxidation state in other elements, example where no corresponding oxide is known include PtF_6 and AuF_5.

Halides and Halide Complexes

Almost all elements form thermodynamically stable halides. The normal stability sequence is F > Cl > Br > I, which in covalent compounds follows the expected order of bond strengths, and in ionic compounds that of the lattice energies. The thermodynamic stability of fluorides (and the kinetic reactivity of F_2) is also aided by the weak F–F bond. Many halides can be made by direct combination, but fluorinating agents such as ClF_3 are sometimes used in preference to F_2, which is very difficult to handle.

The structural and bonding trends in halides follow similar patterns to those in oxides. Most nonmetallic elements form simple molecular compounds in which atoms each have a single bond to other element. This is true also for metals in high oxidation states (*e.g.* $TiCl_4$ and UG_6). The compounds may be solids, liquids or gases, with volatility in the order F > Cl > Br > I as expected from the strength of van der Waals' forces. In the hydrogen halides HF is exceptional because of strong hydrogen bonding a weak acid in water, the other HX compounds being strong acids.

Covalent halides are less often polymeric in structure than oxides, a difference partly caused by the different stoichiometries (*e.g.*, SiF_4 versus SiO_2), which provide a higher coordination number in the monomeric molecular halides. However, the halides of some metals (*e.g.* beryllium;) may be better considered as polymeric than ionic. Some molecular halides of both metallic and non-metallic elements form halogen-bridged dimers and higher oligomers (*e.g.* Al_2Cl_6).

Most metallic elements form solid halides with structures expected for **ionic solids**. Structural differences often occur with MX_2 and MX_3, fluorides more often having rutile, fluorite or rhenium trioxide structures and the heavier halides layer structures. These differences reflect the more ionic nature of fluorides, and the higher polarizability of the larger halide ions. Many halides are very soluble in water, but low solubilities are often found with fluorides of M^{2+} and M^{3+} ions (*e.g.* CaF_2, AlF_3), and with heavier halides of less electropositive metals (*e.g.* AgCl, TlCl). These differences are related to lattice energy trends.

Many halides of metals and nonmetals are good Lewis acids. Such compounds are generally hydrolyzed by water, and also form halide complexes (*e.g.* $AlCl_4^{2-}$, PF^-), which can make useful counterions in solid with large or strongly oxidizing cations. Both cations and anionic complexes may be formed by halide transfer, for example, in solid PCl_5 (Topic F6) and in liquid BrF_3 (see below). Many metal ions also form halide complexes in aqueous solution. For a majority of elements the flouoride complexes are more stable but softer or class b metals form stronger complexes with heavier halides.

Oxides and Oxoacids

I_2O_5 is the only halogen oxide of moderate thermodynamic stability. Other compounds include X_2O (not I), X_2O_2 (F and Cl), the odd-electron XO_2 (Cl and Br), and CL_2O_7. Most of these compounds are strongly oxidizing, have low thermal stability and can decompose explosively. ClO_2 is used as a bleaching agent.

Except for fluorine the elements have an extensive oxoacid chemistry. Figure shows Frost diagrams with the oxidation states found in acid and alkaline solution. The sharp trend in oxidizing power of the elements (X_2/X^- potential) can be seen. As expected from Pauling's rules the **hypohalous acids** X(OH) and **chlorous acid** ClO(OH) are weak acids, but the halic acids XO_2(OH) and especially **perchloric acid** ClO_3(OH) and perbromic acid are strong. **Periodic acid** is exceptional, as, although periodates containing the tetrahedral IO_4^- ion are known, the predominant form in water is the octahedral $IO(OH)_5$, which, as expected is a weak acid.

The redox behaviour is strongly pH dependent but is also influenced by kinetic factors. From the pH = 14 diagram in Fig. 6.5 it can be seen that Cl_2 and Br_2 disproportionate in alkaline solution. The thermodynamically expected products are X^- and XO_3^- but the hypochlorite ion ClO^- is formed in cold conditions, and further disproportionation occurs on heating.

The perhalic acids and their anions are strong oxidizing agents, especially BrO_4^-, which is not thermodynamically stable in aqueous solution. They do, however have considerable kinetic stability. Perchlorates of organic or organometallic cations are very dangerous as they may appear stable, but can explode unpredictably with extreme force.

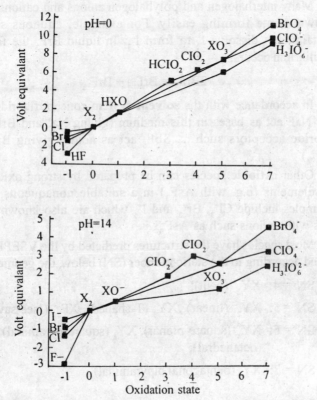

Fig. 6.4. Frost diagrams for the halogens in aqueous solution at pH = 0 (a) and pH = 14 (b). X represents any halogen, except F for positive oxidation states.

Interhalogen and Polyhalogen Compounds

Binary compounds known as **interhalogen compounds** with stiochiometry XY_n are found between every pair of halogens F–I. For neutral molecules n is an odd number and when $n > 1$ the terminal atom Y is always the lighter element. The maximum n found with a given pair increases with the difference in period number, some examples being Ibr, ICl_3, BrF_3 and IF_7. Most interhalogen compounds are obtained by direct reaction. They are strongly oxidizing and the fluorides are good fluorinating agents.

Many interhalogen and polyhalogen anions and cations are also known, some forming easily. For example, aqueous solutions containing I^- dissolve I_2 to form I^-_3. In liquid BrF_3 the following equilibrium occurs:

$$2BrF_3 = BrF^+_2 + BrF^-_4$$

In accordance with the **solvent-system** concept fluoride donors like NaF act as bases in this medium (giving Na^+ and BrF^-_4), and fluoride acceptors such as SbF_5 act as acids (giving BrF^+_2 and SbF^-_4).

Other **cationic species** can be prepared by strong oxidation of the elements (e.g. with AsF_3) in a suitable nonaqueous solvent. Examples include Cl^+_3, Br^+_2 and I^+_5 which are also known in solid salts with an ions such as AsF^-_6.

Most species have the structures predicted by the VSEPR model. Listed according to the steric number (SN) below, the geometries are

SN = 4: XY_2^+ (bent);

SN = 5: XY_2^- (linear), XY_3 (T-shaped), XF_4^+ ('see-saw');

SN = 6: XY_4^- (square-planar), XY_5 (square-pyramidal), XY_6^+ (octahedral);

SN = 7: XY_7 (pentagonal bipyramidal)

6.10 Noble Gases

The group 18 of the periodic table includes six elements–helium, neon, argon, krypton, xenon and radon. These are gases at ordinary temperature and are devoid of chemical activity for which reason they are commonly known as *noble gases*. Previously they were called *inert gases*. However, of a late a number of xenon and krypton compounds have been prepared and these demets are therefore not inert. The term *noble gases* is hence preferred over the term inert gases. None of these elements was known in the times of Mendeleeff and their introduction in the so called zero group was made at a later stage.

As is seen from the their configurations all these elements are characterized by an external most shell of eight electrons, *i.e.*, s^2p^6 arrangement with the exception of helium which has only two electrons in its outermost shell $1s^2$. The chemical inertness of these elements is attributed to this peculiar arrangement, *i.e.*, to the 'closed' structure of eight electrons. In the modern theory of atomic structure and valence, the number and arrangement of the electrons in the atom of group 18 elements is taken as a model of greatest stability and the atoms of other elements are presumed to enter into chemical combination in order to attain a configuration of this type. *Thus the elements of the group 18 have made an important contribution towards an understanding of the atomic structure and the electronic theory of valence.* Since the external shells of these elements contain the full quota of electrons, they can neither accept nor donate any electron and are, therefore, zero-valent. However, some compounds of these elements have recently been prepared which indicate that they do have low reactivity.

These elements are gases and also known as **rare gases** because of their being present in very small amounts in air.

The Monoatomic Nature of the Noble gases. In the absence of the chemical evidence, the monoatomicity of the Nobel gases has been deduced from the following facts:

(i) The ratio of their specific or molar heats at constants pressure and at constant volume, *i.e.*, C_p/C_v is 1.67.

(ii) The refractive indices, dielectric constants and other physical properties of the noble gases also correspond to their monoatomic state.

The gases are not generally abundant on Earth, although argon (formed by the radioactive decay of ^{40}K) makes up about 1 mol % of the atmosphere, and helium (formed by radioactive decay or uranium and thorium; occurs in natural gas. Radon is radioactive, ^{222}Rn with a half-life 3.8 days also being formed by radioactive decay from ^{238}U. The boiling points of the elements show the trend expected from van der Waals' forces that of helium (4.2 K) being the lowest of any substances. Helium is also unique as it does not solidity except under pressure; the remaining elements form monatomic solids with close-packed structures. Liquid helium is used for maintaining very low temperatures (*e.g.* for superconducting magnets), argon as an inert gas in some metallurgical processes, and all the elements in gas discharge tubes.

$$:\overset{+}{\underset{..}{\ddot{X}e}} - \ddot{\underset{..}{F}}:$$

With their closed-shell electron configurations the noble gas elements of group 18 were long regarded as chemically inert. However, in 1962 Barlett noted that the ionization energy of xenon was similar to that of O_2, and by reaction with PtF_6 attempted to prepare the compound analogous to $[O_2]^+[PtF_6]^-$. He obtained a complex product containing the ion $[XeF]^+$ (with a valence structure 1 isoelectronic to dihalogen molecules) rather than the expected Xe^+. Many compounds of xenon are now known, mostly with F and O, and few of Krypton.

Xenon Compounds

The binary fluorides XeF_2, XeF_4 and XeF_6 are thermodynamically stable and can be prepared by direct reaction under appropriate conditions. They are reactive fluorinating agents. The bonding can be described by three-centre molecular orbital pictures or by resonance structures (*e.g.* 2) in which no valence-shell expansion is required. The structures of XeF_2 (linear) and XeF_4 (square-planar) are those expected in the VSEPR model but that of gas-phase XeF_6 has proved elusive. It is believed that (as predicted for a molecule with a lone-pair) the shape is not a regular octahedron, but that **fluxional processes** lead to a rapid interchange between different distorted configurations. In the solid structure, some association between molecules occurs and the geometry around Xe is distorted, as expected in the VSEPR theory.

$$\overset{-}{F} \qquad \overset{+}{Xe} - F$$

2

Compounds that appear to contain the $[XeF]^+$ (1) and bent $[Xe_2F_3]^+$ ions are known although the former is always strongly coordinated to a counterions such as SbF_6^-. Complex anions include XeF_5^-, XeF_7^-, and XeF_8^{2-}, the first of which has a unique pentagonal planar structure (3), as expected from VSEPR.

$$\left[\begin{array}{c} F \\ F \diagdown \diagup \\ Xe - F \\ F \diagup \diagdown \\ F \end{array} \right]^-$$

3

Oxohalides such as $XeOF_4$ are known. Hydrolysis of XeF_6 gives XeO_3, which disproportionates in alkaline solution:

$$2XeO_3 + 4OH^- \rightarrow 2HXeO_4^- + 2OH^- \rightarrow XeO_6^{4-} + Xe + O_2 + 2H_2O$$

Salts containing the octahedral Xe^{VIII} **perxenate ion** XeO_6^{4-} are known, and by the action of acid the tetrahedral **xenon teroxide** XeO_4 is formed.

All xenon-oxygen compounds are very strongly oxidizing, and some decompose explosively. Compounds with Xe—O bonds attaching polyatomic groups are known, and weak Xe—N and Xe—C bonds can also be formed, as in $Xe(CF_3)_2$, which decomposes rapidly at room temperature.

Krypton Compounds

No krypton compounds appear to thermodynamically stable, but KrF_2 can be made from the elements in an electric discharge at very low temperatures, and a few compounds of the cationic species $[KrF]^+$ and $[Kr_2F_3]^+$ are also known. As the ionization energy of Kr is higher than that of Xe, the lower stability of krypton compounds is expected from the bonding models shown in structures 1 and 2, where Xe carries a formal positive charge.

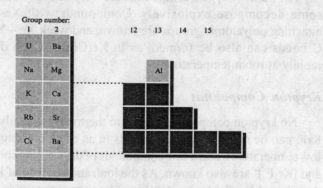

7

Non-Transition Metals

7.1 Introduction

The position of non-transition metals in the periodic table is shown in Fig. 7.1.

Fig. 7.1. Position of non-transition metals in the periodic table, with post-transition metals shaded.

They can be further classified as (i) Pre-transition metals, (ii) Post-transition metals.

(i) **The pre-transition** metal of group 1 and group 2; and Al (aluminium) is group 13. They are also **typical metals**. They show their expected oxidation state (e.g. Na^+, Mg^{2+}, Al^{3+}).

Group 12 atoms have the electron configuration $((n-1)d)^{10}(ns)^2$ and also form positive ions M^{2+} by removal of the s electrons. Filling the d shell from Ca to Zn involves an increase of effective nuclear charge that raises the ionization energy and reduces the ionic radius. Lattice energies for Zn^{2+} are expected to be somewhat larger than for Ca^{2+}, and the formation Zn^{2+} is also assisted by the slightly lower sublimation energy of metallic zinc. Nevertheless, these factors do not compensate fully for the increased ionization energy, and so zinc is less electropositive (less negative E^θ value) than calcium. On descending group 12, ionization energies do not decrease to compensate for smaller lattice energies as they do in group 12, and E^θ values increase down the group. This is particularly marked with mercury, where especially high ionization energies result from the extra nuclear charge consequent on filling the $4f$ shell in the sixth period, combined with relativistic effects.

Group Trends

From above analysis it is clear that electropositive character remains strong throughout pre-transition groups. The major vertical trends in the stability and structure of compounds result from the changing ionic size. The small radius of Li^+ and Be^{2+} gives some peculiarities, which are sometimes known as diagonal relationships. Thus the solubilities and thermal stabilities of lithium compounds are often closer to those of magnesium than to those of other group 1 elements. Beryllium has even more marked differences from the rest of group 2, showing similarities with its diagonal neighbour aluminium. These relationships can be related to the size of charge and ratio of ions. The small ions Li^+ give lattice and solvation energies more similar to Mg^{2+} than to Na^+. The very small Be^{2+} is comparable with Al^{3+} in its polarizing power, which produces deviations from ionic character in solid-state and solution chemistry.

Size also increases down post-transition metal groups but the chemical trends are less regular. Solid compounds often have lower coordination numbers than expected by comparison with pre-transition metal ions of smaller size, and have patterns stability and solubility that suggest an appreciable degree of covalent bonding. The changing balance between ionization and lattice (or solvation) energies also has the consequence that lower oxidation states become more favourable. These tendencies are especially marked in period 6 (Hg, Tl, Pb, Bi). Thus many Tl^I and Pb^{II} compounds are known, the states Tl^{III} and Pb^{VI} being strongly oxidizing (see further discussion in Topic G5). The **inert-pair effect** is a somewhat misleading term for this phenomenon, implying the existence of an electron pair $(ns)^2$ too tightly bound to be involved in bonding. In fact, the 'inert pair' can have important structural consequences (see Topic G6). The discussion above also emphasizes that the relatively stability of oxidation states always depends on a balance of factors, not on ionization energies alone.

Non-cationic Chemistry

Although cationic chemistry has been emphasized above, other types of bonding are possible with the elements of all groups in this section. These include the following:

- **Covalent compounds.** Compounds with predominantly covalent character include organometallic compounds.
- **Anionic compounds.** Under unusual conditions, group 1 elements can form anions such as Na^-. Some post-transition elements form polyatomic ions.
- **Metal-metal bonding.** This is especially a feature of post-transition groups and can accompany many 'unusual' oxidation states, of which Hg^I (in fact Hg^{2+}_2) is the commonest example.

7.2. Alkali Metals

The elements of group 1 (Li, Na, K, Rb, Cs, Fr) are collectively known as **alkali metals.** They occur in nature only as +1 ions. They are the most electropositive in nature and their compounds are most ionic. The salts of alkali metals are quite soluble in water and thus they are found in large quantities in water and salt deposits which have formed by the evaporation of brine. However many in soluble clays also contain alkali metals as complex metal silicates.

Li, Rb and Cs are of lower abundance and are obtained from silicate minerals. Francium (Fr) is a radioactive element and occurs in very small quantities in uranium minerals. The longest-lived isotope of francium is ^{223}Fr ($t_{1/2} = 22$ min).

Alkali metals are soft, have low m.p. and are strong reducing agents.

Table 7.1. Properties of alkali metals; melting and boiling points, atomization and ionization enthalpies, ionic and standard electrode potentials

Element	MP(C)	BP(C)	DH (KJ mol^{-1})	I (KJ mol^{-1})	r(M$^+$) (pm)	E^0(M$^+$/M) (V)
Li	180	1347	162	520	76	−3.03
Na	98	881	110	496	102	−2.71
K	63	765	90	419	138	−2.92
Rb	39	688	88	403	152	−2.93
Cs	28	705	79	376	167	−2.92

Solution Chemistry

Aqueous chemistry is entirely dominated by the M$^+$ ions. The M$^+$/M electrode potentials are all extremely negative (see Table 7.1), that of Li being slightly more so than the others because of the large solvation energy as a result of its small size. The higher solvation of lithium can be seen in the **ionic mobilities** determined from the ionic conductivities of dissolved salts. It might be expected that the smallest ion would be the most mobile, but in fact Li$^+$ is the least mobile and it appears that the smallest 'bare' ion becomes the largest on solvation.

The M$^+$ ions have only weak complexing tendencies, but these can be enhanced by suitably sized **macrocyclic ligands**. Ligands with different cavity sizes can be used to discriminate between alkali ions.

The metallic elements dissolve in **liquid ammonia** and related amines (*e.g.* ethylamine $C_2H_5NH_2$) to give solutions which contain **solvated electrons** in addition to cations. In some solvents there is evidence for equilibria involving alkali anions M$^-$. The solutions are useful reducing agents for the preparation of unusually low oxidation states (*e.g.* [Ni^0(CN$_4$)]$^{4-}$) including anionic compounds of the alkali elements themselves.

Solid Compounds

The alkali metals react with many other elements directly to make binary solids. The **alkali halides** are often regarded as the most 'typical' ionic solids. Their lattice energies agree closely with calculations although their structures do not all conform to the simple radius ratio rules, as all have the rocksalt (NaCl) structure at normal temperature and pressure, except CsCl, CsBr and CsI, which have the eight-coordinate CsCl structure. The alkali halides are all moderately soluble in water, LiF being the least so.

The elements also form **hydrides** by direct interaction between the elements LiH is the most stable and is a useful precursor for other hydrides. Lithium also reacts with N_2 to form the nitride Li_3N.

The elements form **oxides** M_2O, which have the antiflourite structure for li-Rb. Cs_2O has the very unusual anti-CdI_2 structure with adjacent layers of Cs^+ (see Topic D4). All compounds are very basic and react with water and CO_2 to produce hydroxides and carbonates, respectively. Except for Li, however, the simple oxides are not the normal products of burning the elements in air, K, Rb and Cs form **superoxides** MO_2 containing the O_2 ion, and sodium the **peroxides** Na_2O_2 with O_2^{2-}. The relative stability of these compounds with large cations of low charge can be understood by lattice energy arguments (see Topic D6 and F7). Rb and Cs also form **suboxides** when oxygen supply is very deficient, for example, Rb_2O_2 (1) and $Cs_{11}O_3$; the structure of the former compound is based on two face-sharing octahedral with direct Rb–Rb bonding giving distances shorter than in the metallic element.

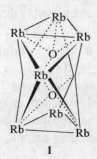

1

Hydroxides MOH are important compounds for all the alkali metals. They can easily formed by reaction of oxides with water (or atmosphere moisture). They are soluble in water and give **strong base**. Compounds of oxoacids are commonly encountered, such as carbonate, nitrate, sulphate, etc. as these anions are fairly large, lithium compounds tend to be the most soluble in the series. Many of these compounds crystallize in a variety of hydrated forms (*e.g.* $Na_2CO_3 \cdot nH_2O$ with $n = 1$, 7 or 10).

The combination of the reducing power of alkali metal-ammonia solutions with the strong complexing power of macrocyclic ligands allows compounds to be made containing unusual anions, such as $[Sn_9]^{4-}$. Among the unexpected products of such reactions are **alkalide** and **electride** salts. An example of an alkalide is $[Na(2.2.2.crypt)]^+$ Na^-, where crypt is the cryptand ligand 2. The crystal structure shows that the Na^- ion is larger than I^-. In electrides such as $[CS(18\ crown-6)_2]^+e^-$ there is a 'bare' electron trapped in a cavity in the lattice.

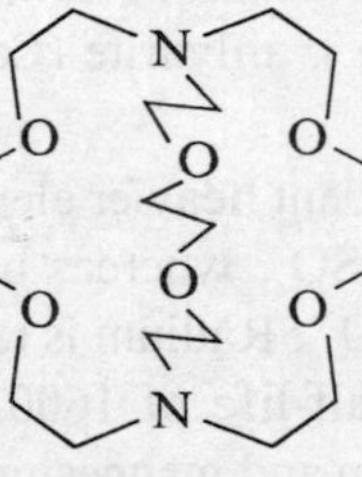

2

Organometallic Compounds

Lithium is exceptional in forming molecular alkyls with oligomeric structures, for example, the tetrameric $Li_4(CH_3)_4$ (3). Bonding in the 'cubane'-like framework is provided by delocalised electrons. These compounds may be prepared by direct reaction between Li metal and alkyl halides and are useful reagents for preparing organometallic compounds of other elements, and as alternatives to Grignard reagents in organic synthesis. Organometallic compounds of the other elements form solids with somewhat more ionic character.

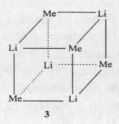

3

7.3 Alkaline Earths

The elements of group 2 (Be, Mg, Ca, Ba, Sr, Rn) are known as **alkaline earth metals** or **alkaline earths**. These metals occur only as +2 ions. They exist as carbonates sulphates and silicates. Magnesium is eighth most abundant element in earth's crust. It occurs as $MgCO_3$ (Magnesite) dolomite ($MgCO_3$ $CaCO_3$) and a silicate minerals such as asbestos ($3AgSiO_3$ $CaSiO_3$) and magnesium ions in sea water.

Calcium in fifth in abundance in earth's crust and occurs as chalk, limestone, marble ($CaCO_3$), anlydrite ($CaSO_4$) and gypsum ($CaSO_4$ $2H_2O$).

The moderately abundant heavier elements are found principally as sulfates $SrSO_4$ and $BaSO_4$, whereas beryllium is rather rare and occurs in beryl $Be_3Al_2Si_6O_{18}$. Radium is radioactive, its longest-lived isotope ^{226}Ra having a half-life of 1600 years and being found in uranium minerals. Calcium and magnesium are major elements in life but beryllium and its compounds are very toxic.

The metallic elements are all potentially very reactive towards air, water and most elements, but Be and Mg form passivating oxide films. Elemental magnesium is manufactured in large quantities either by electrolysis of molten MgCl or by reduction of MgO, and is used in lightweight alloys and as a reducing agent. The other elements are used mainly as compounds.

Beryllium ion (Be^{2+}) is very small having high polarizing power. It forms compound with more covalent character and its compounds show similarity with those of aluminium and with group 12 element Zn.

Solution and Coordination Chemistry

The properties of M^{2+} aqueous show trends expected from their increasing size down the group, Be^{2+} (like Al^{3+}) is **amphoteric.** The insoluble hydroxide dissolves in both acid solution:

$$Be(OH)_2 + 2H_2O + 2H^+ \rightarrow [Be(H_2O)_4]^{2+}$$

and in alkaline conditions:

$$Be(OH)_2 + 2OH^- \rightarrow [Be(OH)_4]^{2-}$$

The simple aqua cation is present only in strongly acidic conditions. As the pH increases, successive protolysis and polymerization reactions first give soluble species with Be–OH–Be bridges, and then the solid hydroxide. The other M^{2+} ions are basic. As the hydroxide $M(OH)_2$ becomes more soluble in the series Mg < Ca <Sr < Ba precipitation requires increasingly high pH.

Complex formation is dominated by class **a** or '**hard**' behaviour and is generally most favourable for the smaller ions. Beryllium forms $[BeF_4]^{2-}$ and strong complexes with some bidentate ligands such as oxalate $C_2O_4^{2-}$. From carboxylic acids unusual complexes such as $[Be_4O(O_2CCH_3)_6]$ can be obtained; the structure (1) has a central oxygen atom surrounded by a Be_4 tetrahedron with acetate groups bridging the edges (only one shown). The larger ions form complexes with chelating ligands such as EDTA. Complexes with ammonia such as $[Mg(NH_3)_6]^{2+}$ can be made in nonaqueous conditions but are not stable in water. However, **chlorophylls,** which are essential for photosynthesis in all green plants, have magnesium coordinated by nitrogen in macrocyclic porphine derivatives: 2 shows the basic framework, which has other organic groups attached; Mg^{2+} normally has one water molecule also coordinated.

1

2

Solid Compounds

Binary compounds are formed with all nonmetallic elements, many by direct combination. Beryllium is exceptional as its coordination is almost tetrahedral, giving structures that may be regarded as polymeric rather than highly ionic. Thus BeO has the wuartzite structure, BeF_2 is similar to SiO_2, and $BeCl_2$ (like SiS_2) has a chain structure (3) based on edge-sharing tetrahedral, BeH_2 is similar, with bridging hydrogens forming three-centre bonds as in B_2H_6.

Compounds of the remaining elements have structures more in line with the expectations of the ionic model. Oxides MO all have the rocksalt structure; as the cation size increases they become increasingly basic and reactive towards water and CO_2, giving $M(OH)_2$ or MCO_3, respectively. **Peroxides** such as BaO_2 are formed by the heavier elements in the group. **Halides** show increasing coordination with size, six for Mg and seven or eight for the larger ions, MgF_2 has the rutile structure and the other Mf_2 compounds the fluorite structure. Heavier halides of Mg give layer structures ($CdCl_2$ and CdI_2) whereas for the larger cations somewhat distorted structures are formed (*e.g.* distorted rutile for $CaCl_2$); these appear to be dictated by the tendency to asymmetrical coordination of the halide ion, with cations too large to form normal layer structures. Fluorides (especially CaF_2) have low solubility in water, but other halides are extremely soluble.

Binary compounds with less electronegative elements include hydrides, nitrides, sulfides and phosphides. They are decomposed by water and can provide convenient routes for the preparation of nonmetal hydrides. The anions may be polyatomic or polymerized, as with CaC_2, which contains C_2^{2-} and reacts with water to give acetylene (ethyne) C_2H_2.

The elements form an enormous range of compounds with **oxoanions,** many of those with calcium (carbonate, silicate, phosphate, sulfate) being common minerals in the Earth's crust. Hydrated forms are common. Their thermal stability towards decomposition to the oxide is less than that for the alkali metals, and increases with cation size. Thus Be (like Al) does not form a stable carbonate; the decomposition temperatures for the other range from 400°C for $MgCO_3$ to 1400°C for $BaCO_3$. These trends can be understood using lattice energy arguments.

Organometallic Compounds

Be and Mg form an extensive range of organometallic compounds, those of Ca, Sr, and Ba being much more reactive and difficult to characterize. Beryllium alkyls such as $Be(CH_3)_2$ have chain structures (see 3 with X = CH_3) with multicentre bonding similar to that in $Li_4(CH_3)_4$ and $Al_2(CH_3)_6$. Be and Mg from biscyclopentadienyl compounds $M(C_5H_5)_2$; the Mg compound has an η^5 sandwich structure like that of ferrocene but is more reactive and at least partially ionic: $M^{2+}(C_5H_5)_2$. The Be compound is less symmetrical with one ring displaced sideways, presumably because of the small size of Be.

$$\underset{\textbf{3}}{X\cdots \underset{Be}{\diagdown} \cdots X \cdots \underset{Be}{\diagdown} \cdots X \cdots \underset{Be}{\diagdown} \cdots X \cdots \underset{Be}{\diagdown} \cdots}$$

By far the most commonly encountered organometallic compounds in group 2 are the **Grignard reagent** RMgX, formed by reaction of Mg metal with an alkyl or aryl halide RX in an ether solvent. Solid compounds with additional ether molecules coordinated to Mg can be obtained, but the reagents are generally used in solution. They are very useful for alkylation and arylation reactions, either for forming C–C bonds in organic chemistry, or for preparing organometallic compounds of other elements.

7.4. Zinc, Cadmium and Mercury

(Metals of Group 12)

The elements are found in nature as sulfides, especially ZnS (zinc blende or sphalerite) and HgS (cinnabar). Overall abundance in the crust are low. Zinc is an important element of life; Cd and Hg are not essential and are very toxic.

The elements may be obtained by reduction of sulfides or oxides (*e.g.* ZnO with C). Zinc and cadmium are used for corrosion-resistant coatings. The metals have melting and boiling points that are lower than for group 2 elements, especially with Hg, which is one of two elements (Br being the other) existing as a liquid at 25°C. Zn and Cd are more reactive than Hg, dissolving in non-oxidizing acids and forming oxide films in air. Mercury oxidizes at room temperature but HgO decomposes readily on heating, a reaction historically important in the discovery of oxygen. Mercury dissolves many metallic elements to form **amalgama,** which can be useful reagents (*e.g.* sodium amalgam as a reducing agent, being much easier to handle than elemental sodium).

M^{II} Solution Chemistry

The aqua ions M^{2+} are more acidic than those in the same periods in group 2 (see Topic E2). Zinc (like Be) is amphoteric, dissolving at high pH to form $[Zn(OH)_4]^{2-}$. The other ions are not amphoteric as they have little tendency to complex with the hard ion OH⁻, but Hg^{2+} is very strongly protolyzed and readily precipitates as HgO unless complexing ligands are present.

All the ions can form string complexes, the overall formation constants for tetrahedral $[ML_4]$ species (*e.g.,* $[HgCl_4]^{2-}$) with a selection of ligands, being shown in Table 7.2. There is an increasing tendency to 'soft' class b behaviour in the order Zn < Cd << Hg. Complexes with Hg^{2+} are among the strongest known with any element. In addition to the $[Ml_4]$ complexes, mercury can form linear $[HgL_2]$ and sometimes $[HgL_3]$. As in the solid compounds, these trends indicate a pronounced tendency to covalent bonding; or grounds of size alone, the large Hg^{2+} ion could support a coordination number of six or even eight.

M^{II} Solid Compounds

Only the **Fluorides** have structures and properties expected for ionic compounds with cations of the appropriate size (ZnF_2 rutile, the others fluorite). In other compounds the characteristic coordination numbers are four for Zn, four or six for Cd, and two or four for Hg.

Zn and Cd **halides** (apart from fluorides) are based on close-packed lattices of halide ions, with Zn occupying tetrahedral holes and Cd octahedral ones. The Zn compounds are best regarded as polymeric, whereas those of Cd are prototypes of the important $CdCl_2$ and CdI_2 **layer structures**. Both sets of compounds are soluble, in water, but solutions of Cd halides contains a variety of complex ions $[CdX_n]$ in equilibrium. Hg halides have varying coordination, with two close neighbours in $HgCl_2$ making this compound essentially molecular, the others being more polymeric. Solubility in water is low but increases markedly with rise in temperature giving undissociated HgX_2 molecules.

Among the **oxides and sulfides**, only CdO adopts the octahedral rocksalt structure found with group 2 element, although the solid is normally very deficient in oxygen and the electrons not used in bonding give rise to metallic properties. ZnO and ZnS are prototypes of the tetrahedrally coordinated **wurtzite** and **zinc blende** (or **sphalerite**) structures; in fact, ZnS can adopt either structure, as can CdS and CdSe. HgO and HgS have chain structures with linear two-coordination of Hg.

Table 7.2. Overall equilibrium constants ($log_{10}b_4$) for the formation of some [ML$_4$] complexes.

ligand (L)	Zn^{2+}	$log_{10}\beta_4$ Cd^{2+}	Hg^{2+}
Cl^-	0	3	15
Br^-	−1	4	21
I^-	−2	6	30
NH_3	9	7	19
CN^-	21	19	41

Many of these compounds are coloured and show electronic properties characteristic of small bandgaps and nonstoichiometry.

Lower Oxidation States

The +1 oxidation state is fairly stable for mercury, and invariably involves the dimeric $[Hg–Hg]^{2+}$ ion. Evidence for this comes from solid-state structures, and in solution from many sources:

- Hg^I species are diamagnetic whereas Hg^+ would have an unpaired electron;
- Raman spectra of solutions show a band from Hg–Hg stretching vibration similar to that seen in solids;

- Equilibrium studies (*e.g.* by electrochemistry) are consistent with

$$Hg^{2+}_2(aq) \longrightarrow Hg(l) + Hg^{2+}(aq)$$

with an equilibrium constant $[Hg^{2+}]/[Hg^{2+}_2] \doteq 0.011$ at 25°C. The equilibrium expression involving Hg^+ would have a different form.

Uncomplexed Hg^{2+}_2 is marginally stable in aqueous, but the disproportionation equilibrium can be upset by any ligands for which the Hg^{II} compound is more stable. Thus addition of sulfide, cyanide and many other ligands causes disproportionation. In solid compounds the Hg^{2+}_2 ion always has two ligands strongly bonded. For example, Hg_2Cl_2 has linear Cl–Hg–Hg–Cl molecules, and salts with noncomplexing anions such as nitrate contain the hydrated ion [H_2O–Hg–Hg–H_2O]$^{2+}$.

Oxidation of Hg with AsF_5 gives species containing linear Hg^{2+}_3 and Hg^{2+}_4 ions, culminating in a metallic compound $Hg_{0.33}AsF_6$, which contains linear chains of mercury atoms.

Zn and Cd analogs of Hg^{2+}_2 are much less stable, principally because the larger lattice energies obtained with the smaller M^{2+} ions tend to force disproportionation (see Topic D6). Zn^{2+}_2 can both be identified spectroscopically when the elements react with melts of the corresponding chloride. Adding $AlCl_3$ gives the solid compound $[Cd_2^{2+}][AlCl_4^-]_2$ but no solid zinc (I) compounds have been prepared.

Organometallic Compounds

The elements form compounds R_2M and RMX, where R is an alkyl or aryl group and X a halide. M–C bond strengths are in the order Zn > Cd > Hg but nevertheless the mercury compounds are the most easily formed; for example, from

$$RH + HgX_2 \rightarrow RHgX + HX$$

The Hg compounds are also the least reactive towards air or water, partly because the competing Hg–O bond is so much weaker than with Zn or Cd, they are useful for preparing organometallic compounds of other elements. Water-soluble ions can be obtained, such as [CH_3Hg]$^+$, which has been used as a prototype 'soft' acid in the hard and soft acid and base (HSAB) classification (see Topic C8).

All organomercury compounds are **extremely toxic**, as they pass through cell membranes much more easily than inorganic forms.

7.5 Aluminium and Thallium

Group 13 Metals

Aluminium (Al) does not occur in free state in nature. In the combined state it is the third most abundant element found in nature, the first two being oxygen and silicon. Aluminium forms 7-8% of earth's crust. It is a constituent of clay, slate and many types of silicate rocks. It occurs as *corundium* (Al_2O_3), *diaspore* ($Al_2O_3H_2O$), bauxite ($Al_2O_3 2H_2O$), *cryolite* (Na_3AlF_6), *feldspar* ($KAl Si_3O_8$), *aluxite* or *alum stone* [$K_2SO_4 Al_2(SO_4)_3 . 4Al(SO_4)_3$], *Turquoise* [$(AlPO_4).Al(OH)_3. H_2O$] etc.

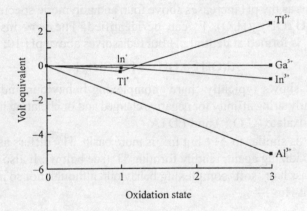

Fig. 7.3. Frost diagram showing the oxidation states of Al, Ga, In, Tl in aqueous solution at pH = 0.

Ga, In and Tl are much less common element obtained in small amounts from sulphides minerals of other elements the +3 oxidation state. The group trends are very different, however, from those in groups 1 and 2. The Al^{3+} ions has a large charge/radius ratio and is strongly polarizing, so that significant deviations from simple ionic behaviour are often observed. The filling of the *d* shells (and 4*f* in period 6) leads to decreased electropositive character for Ga, In and

Tl similar to that shown in group 12. There is also a progressive stabilization of lower oxidation states down the group.

Aluminium is quite reactive when clean, the metal easily form a very resistant oxide film, which allows it use in a number of applications as a light weight construction material and in cooking and other vessels.

Ga, In and Tl are used only in specialized applications. These metals are less reactive than aluminium. The **frost diagram** shown in Fig. 7.3 shows much larger negative slope (negative electride potential) of aluminium. The compounds of thallium (Tl) are toxic but they pose no environmental hazard as they are little used.

M^{III} Aqueous Chemistry

Al^{3+} is **amphoteric** and will dissolve in acidic and alkaline solutions. The $[Al(H_2O)_6]^{3+}$ ion is formed at low pH but undergoes increasing protolysis as the pH increases above four, and polymeric species such as $[Al_{13}O_4(OH)_{24}(H_2O)_{12}]^{7+}$ can be identified. The very insoluble $Al(OH)_3$ is formed at neutral pH but redissolves above pH 10:

$$Al(OH)_3 + OH^- \rightarrow [Al(OH)_4^-]$$

Al^{3+} shows typically 'hard' complexing behaviour and has a particularly string affinity for negative charged and.or chelating ligands, such as oxalate $(C_2O_4^{2-})$ and EDTA.

Ga^{3+} is similar to Al^{3+} but In^{3+} is more basic. Tl^{3+} differs as it is a strong oxidizing agent, readily forming Tl^+ (see below). It also shows string class b or 'soft' complexing behaviour, although not so marked as that of Hg^{2+}.

M^{III} Compounds

All **aluminium halides** can be obtained by direct reaction, but AlF_3 is best produced by reaction with anhydrous HF. It has a structure based on corner-sharing AlF_6 octahedra (similar to ReO_3). Solid $AlCl_3$ has a polymeric layer structure, but in the gas phase or nonpolar solvents is molecular and dimeric Al_2Cl_4. The bromine and iodide have the molecular dimeric form in the solid state. Aluminium halides are strong Lewis acids and $AlCl_3$ is frequently used as an acid catalyst, e.g. in organic Friedel Craft reactions. Complex halides containing the ions $[AlF_6]^{3-}$ and $[AlCl_4]^-$ are easily formed and can be useful for the preparation of compounds containing unusual cations such as Cd^{2+}_2.

The most stable form of the **oxide Al_2O_3** is α-alumina with the **corundum** structure where Al^{3+} ions occupy two-thirds of the octahedral holes in a hexagonal close-packed oxide lattice. Another form γ-Al_2O_3 has a defect spinel structure (see below). So-called β-**alumina** is in fact a mixed oxide of aluminium of approximate formula $NaAl_{11}O_{17}$ with a disordered arrangement of Na^+ ions, and is a good ionic conductor.

Aluminium forms many mixed oxides of which the **aluminosilicates** are major constituents of minerals. In these compounds aluminium sometimes replaces a portion of the silicon present as corner-sharing SiO_4 groups. The mixed oxide mineral spinel $MgAl_2O_4$ gives its name to an important structure type. One-half of the octahedral holes and one-eighth of the tetrahedral holes are filled in a cubic close-packed array of oxide ions. In the **normal spinel** form adopted by $MgAl_2O_4$ the divalent Mg^{2+} ion is in tetrahedral sites the trivalent Al^{3+} is octahedral. In the defect spinel structure of γ-Al_2O_3 a fraction of the cation sites are occupied at random.

Halides and oxides of Ga and In are fairly similar to those Al, but have less negative enthalpies of formation and (with In) a tendency to higher coordination. Tl^{III} is more strongly oxidizing; for example, there is no Tl^{III} iodide, and the compound of Stoichiometry TlI_3 in fact contains Tl^I with linear tri-iodide ion I_3^-.

Al, Ga and In form tetrahedrally coordinated solids with elements of group 15, which are part of the series of **III-V semiconductor** (*i.e.* groups 13–15). The mixed compounds gallium aluminium phosphides $Ga_{1-r}Al_rP$ and the arsenide $Ga_{1-r}Al_rAs$ are used for light-emitting diode (LED) displays and semiconductor lasers.

Aluminium hydride AlH_3 has a structure to that of AlF_3. The **tetrahydroaluminate ions** $[AlH_4]^-$ is a powerful reducing and hydride transfer agent, generally used in the form of 'lithium aluminium hydride' $LiAlH_4$ made by reaction of LiH with $AlCl_3$. Stability of hydrides decreases down the group but $[GaH_4]^-$ is fairly stable and the unstable diagallane molecule Ga_2H_6 has been identified with a structure like that of diborane.

Organoaluminium compounds are dimeric but the bonding is different from that of halides as the bridging methyl groups in $Al_2(CH_3)_6$ (1) must be held by three-centre two-electron bonds similar to those in dibrane. Organometallic compounds of Ga, In and Tl are less stable than for Al and do not dimerize.

$$
\begin{array}{ccc}
 & H_3C & \\
 & | & \\
H_3C\cdots & C & \cdots CH_3 \\
 & Al \quad Al & \\
H_3C^{\diagup} & C & ^{\diagdown}CH_3 \\
 & | & \\
 & H_3 &
\end{array}
$$

1

Lower Oxidation States

Gas-phase molecules such as AlH, AlCl and AlO are known at high temperatures and low pressures but, as in group 2, disproportionation occurs under normal conditions because of the much higher lattice or solvation energies associated we M^{3+}. As these energies decrease with ion size down to group, the tendency to disproportionation also declines, and lower oxidation states become commoner. Figure Frost diagram shows the possibility of forming In^+ and Tl^+, the formed prone to disproportionation, the latter much more stable. The increasing stability of ions with the $(ns)^2$ configuration in lower periods is often called the **inert-pair** effect. It is particularly marked in period 6 because of the high ionization energies of these elements (see Pb^{II}, Topic G6) but it is important to remember that it depends now on ionization energies alone but on a balance of different energy trends.

Like K^+, which has a very similar size, Tl^+ is very basic in solution, and forms some compounds with similar structures to those of alkali metals (*e.g.* TlCl has the LsCl struture. It has a great affinity for soft ligands, sometimes its solid structures show an irregular coordination suggesting the influence of lone-pair of electrons as with Sn^{II}.

Ga and In form +1 compounds with large low-charged anions, and also some in which the oxidation state is apparently +2 (or sometimes even fractional). The gas-phase M^{2+} ions have the $(ns)^1$

configuration with one unpaired electrons, and in chemical situations always wither disproportionate or form metal-metal bonds. The former possibility leads to **mixed valence compounds** such as 'GaCl$_2$,' (in fact Ga$^+$[Ga^{III}Cl$_4$]$^-$). The alternative gives ions [M–M]$^+$ (isoelectronic to Hg$^{2-}_2$), although they are never found on their own but are always strongly bonded ligands, as in [Ga$_2$Cl$_6$]$^{2-}$ (2) (Note the difference between this structure and that of Ga$_2$Cl$_6$(Al$_2$Cl$_6$), where there are no electrons available for direct Ga–Ga bonding.)

2

All elements of the group form **Zinti compounds** with electropositive metals. Continuous networks of covalently bonded atoms are generally found, rather than the clusters common with group 14. For example, NaAl and NaTl have tetrahedral diamond-like networks of Al or Tl, which can be understood on the basis that Al$^-$ and Tl$^-$ have the same valence electron count as carbon.

7.6 Tin and Lead (Group 14)

Tin. The principal ore of tin is *cassiterite* or *tin stone* SnO$_2$. The miners speak of tinstone as tin or *black tin* to distinguish it from *White tin*, the name given to the metal. Minor deposits as sulphides are also known for tin. Chief suppliers of tin are Malaysia, Indonesia, Thailand (Siam), Bolivia (South America), Nigeria (Africa) and Burma. In India small quantities of tinstone are available in Hazaribagh (Bihar) and Orissa. More than 80% of the world's total requirement of tin is met by South Asia.

Lead. Although lead occurs in nature as the carbonate, *cerrusite*, PbCO$_3$ and the sulphate *anglesite*, PbSO$_4$, the principal ore of lead is *galena*, PbS, which occurs as grayish-black cubical crystals. The chief producing countries are the United States, Spain and Mexico.

Lead deposits, now being exploited in India by the Metal Corporation of India, are located in Udaipur and Jaipur in Rajasthan.

Both Tin and Lead have several stable isotopes. In case of tin there are as many as 10 isotopes.

The isotopes composition of Pb (and thus its atomic mass) varies detectably according to the source, and such variations have been used to estimate the age of rocks and of the Earth.

The elements are readily produced by reduction of their ores and are soft, low-melting, somewhat unreactive metals. Tin is used for plating, and both elements in low-melting alloys (*e.g.* solder) and as many compounds. Applications of lead, however, are declining as its compounds are very toxic. A continuing major use is in **lead-acid batteries,** which depend on two reactions involving the Pb^0, Pb^{II} and Pb^{IV} states:

$$PbO_2(s) + SO^{2-}_2(aq) + 4H^+(aq) + 2e^- = PbSO_4(s) + 2H_2O(l)$$
$$Pb(s) + SO_4^{2-}(aq) = PbSO_4(s) + 2e^-$$

Occurring at different electrodes, these give a cell potential of 2 V, larger than can be obtained easily from any other pair of electrode reactions in aqueous solution.

M^{IV} *Chemistry*

Many binary Sn^{IV} compounds are known. SnO_2 has the rutile structure, and SnX_2 with X = S, Se, Te the CdI_2 layer structure. SnF_4 has a layer structure constructed from corner-sharing octahedra, but other tetrahalides form tetrahedral molecules. The halides are good Lewis acids, especially SnF_4, which forms complexes such as $[SnF_6]^{2-}$.

The Pb^{IV} state is strongly oxidizing and only oxides and fluorides form stable binary compounds PbO_2 and PbF_4 have the same structure as with tin and mixed-valency oxides such as Pb_3O_4 (containing Pb^{IV} and Pb^{II}) are known. Other Pb^{IV} compound include salts containing the $[PbCl_6]^{2-}$ ions as well as some molecular covalent compounds, such the tetraacetate $Pb(CH_3CO_2)_4$ and organometallic compounds.

Neither element shows any simple aqueous chemistry in the M^{IV} state, as the oxides MO_2 are insoluble in water at all pH values. Reaction of SnO_2 in molten KOH gives the octahedral hydroxanion $[Sn(OH)_6]^{2-}$, in contrast to the normal tetrahedral silicates and germinates, but in parallel with isoelectronic compounds such as $Te(OH)_6$ also found in period 5. Other 'stannates' are mixed oxides without discrete oxoanions (*e.g.* $CaSnO_3$ with the perovskite structure).

M^{II} Chemistry

The structural chemistry of Sn^{II} and Pb^{II} compounds is quite complex and different. The M^{2+} ions have the $(ns)^2$ configuration and hence a nonbonding electron pair which can have a stereochemical influence analogous to that in molecules. Thus the structure of SnO (i) shows tin with four oxygen neighbours on one side and a 'vacant' coordination site apparently occupied by the lone-pair. Sn^{II} sulfide and halides have polymeric structures with similar stereochemical features, but Pb^{II} compounds appear to be more ionic, and less influenced by the nonbonding electrons. One form of PbO has the same structures as SnO, but the structures of many other compounds are similar to those found with the larger M^{2+} ions in group 2, examples being PbS (rocksalt) and PbF_2 (fluorite). Solubility patterns of some Pb^{II} salts also parallel those found in group 2 (*e.g.* insoluble sulfate and carbonate) but differences appear with softer anions: thus PbS is insoluble in water, the heavier halides insoluble in cold water but more soluble in hot.

$$\overset{..}{\underset{\underset{\textbf{1}}{O}}{\overset{Sn}{O\diagup\big|\diagdown O}}}$$

The aqueous M^{2+} ions are fairly acidic, Sn^{2+} especially so and shows typical amphoteric behaviour, undergoing strong protolysis to form polymeric hydroxo species, which dissolve in alkali to form the pyramidal $[Sn(OH)_3]^-$. Pb^{2+} forms complexes with a class b pattern of stability analogous to that Cd^{2+} although it does not complex with NH_3 in aqueous solution.

Other Compounds

M^{II} **organometallic compounds** are found with cyclopentadienyl. $Sn(C_5H_5)_2$ has a 'bent sandwich' structure 2, where the stereochemical influence of the lone-pair is apparent. M^{IV} organometallic compounds with M–C σ bonding are extremely varied and include simple tetraalkyls MR_4 and compounds with Sn–Sn bonds similar to those of Si and Ge. Tetraethyl lead has been widely used as a gasoline additive to improve combustion but is being phased out because of the toxic hazard associated with all lead compounds.

2

Reaction of alloys such as $NaSn_x$ with macrocyclic ligands in amine solvents gives compounds containing anionic clusters such as $[Sn_5]^{2-}$, $[Sn_9]^{4-}$ and $[Pb_5]^{2-}$. These have multicentre metal-metal bonding, which can often be rationalized by Wade's rule.

8

Transition Metals

8.1 Introduction

Some of the d-block elements (transition elements) show metallic properties. Such properties include the possibility of variable oxidation states, compounds with spectroscopic, magnetic or structural features resulting from partially occupied d orbitals; an extensive range of complexes and organometallic compounds including ones with very low oxidation state (zero or even negative); and useful catalytic properties shown by metals and by solid or molecular compounds. Different transition metals display these features to different degrees, but together the properties form a sufficiently coherent pattern that the elements are best dealt with by themed Topics rather than individually or as groups.

Although formally part of the d block, the elements of group 12 do not show typical transition metal characteristics, as the d orbitals are too tightly bound to be involved in chemical bonding. These elements are regarded as post-transition metals.

Vertical Trends

Some of the important consequences of the smaller size of $3d$-elements in comparison to $4d$- and $5d$-elements are as follows:

(i) Electron repulsion is large between electrons in $3d$ orbitals.

Exchange even effects are more significant; also, successive ionization energy rise more sharply compared with later series.

(ii) $3d$ orbitals are not much larger than the $3p$ orbitals of the argon core $(3p)^6$. Can overlap with other atoms is hard to achieve, and covalent or metallic bonds involving $3d$ orbitals is weak compared with $4d$ and $5d$.

Another consequence of the IE trend is that higher oxidation states are less stable (more strongly oxidizing) compared with the $4d$ and $5d$ series. For example, group 7 MnO_4^- is much more strongly oxidizing than ReO_4^-, and in-group 8 Fe is unknown although RuO_4 and OsO_4 are stable compounds.

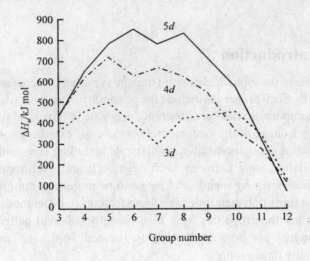

Fig. 8.1. Standard enthalpies of atomization for elements of the three series.

The bond-strength trend $3d \ll 4d \ll 5d$ is the reverse of that normally found for main groups. Its influence can be seen in the atomization enthalpy of the elements, reflecting the strength of bonding in the metallic state, and shown in Fig. 8.1 for elements of the three series. The very high atomization energies of the elements such as tungsten ($5d$ group 6) are reflected in their extremely high melting and boiling points, a property important in applications such as electric light blue filaments. Sublimation energies in the middle of the $3d$ series are much less, partly because the relatively poor overlap of $3d$ orbitals gives weaker bonding and several unpaired electrons (*e.g.,* six with Cr). Compounds with unpaired electron in d orbitals are also much commoner in the $3d$ series, those of the $4d$ series more often forming low-spin configurations or having d electrons involved are metal-metal bonds.

Between the $4d$ and $5d$ series the expected decrease of IEs and increase of radius is counteracted by the increase of nuclear charge involved in filling the $4f$ shell before $5d$. $5d$ elements in early groups are very similar to the corresponding $4d$ ones, although this feature is less marked in later groups.

Horizontal Trends

In each series, the earlier elements can achieve **group oxidation state** corresponding formally to ions with a noble gas configuration (up to Mn^{VII} and Os^{VIII} in $4d$ and $5d$). Increasing effective nuclear charge brings an increase in IEs as shown for the $3d$ elements in Fig. 8.2. Not only does the group oxidation state become very strongly oxidizing for later elements, but redox potentials for any given states (*e.g.,* M^{3+}/M^{2+}) also increase along the series, as the extra lattice or solvation energies of the higher state become less able to compensate for the higher IE values.

With increasing IEs comes also a general decline in electropositive character. Early elements in each series are thermodynamically extremely reactive towards oxygen and other electronegative elements (although the formation of an inert oxide film may kinetically prevent the solid elements from further oxidation). Later elements are less reactive, 2 trend that culminates in the 'noble' or 'coinage' metals Cu, Ag and Au of group 11. The trend is exacerbated in the later $4d$ and $5d$ elements by high atomization energies, and the elements Ru, Rh, Pd, Os, Ir and Pt form a group known as the **platinum metals**, often occurring together in nature, sometimes as metallic alloys. The change in electronegativity is also shown by different patterns of chemical stability: whereas earlier elements of both series generally form more stable compounds with 'harder' anions such as oxide and fluoride (and are found in nature in oxide minerals), the later ones are 'softer' in character and are more often found as sulfides. The trend along the series thus provides a link between the chemical characteristics of the pre-transition and post-transition metals.

A general decline in atomic size is another consequence of increasing effective nuclear charge. Fig. 8.2 also shows the ionic radii of M^{2+} ions of the $3d$ series.

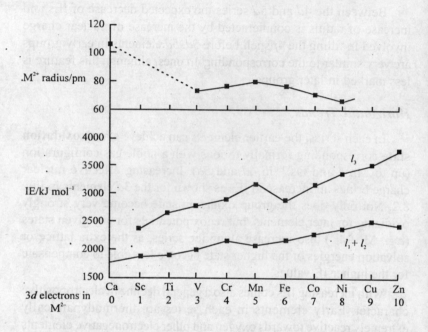

Fig. 8.2. Data for ions of the elements Ca-Zn showing: radii of M^{2+} ions, third IE and the sum of the first and second IEs, and the $(3d)^n$ configurations of M^{2+}.

The expected decrease across the series is modulated by **ligand field Effect.**

Ligand field theory deals with the important consequences of the progressive filling of the d shell. It is normal to specify the d electron number associated with the appropriate transition metal ion, even though the bonding is not assumed to be completely ionic. For example, any Fe^{III} compound is assigned the configuration $(3d)^5$, a Pt^{II} compound $(5d)^8$ (corresponding to Ni^{2+} in the same group). In compounds with very low oxidation states, or with ligands such as organic groups where bonding is largely covalent, a different electron counting scheme is often used. In applying the **18-electron rule** one needs to count the total number of valence electrons in a neutral atom, irrespective of whether they are d or s. This is simply the group number, thus eight for Fe and 10 for Pt. If ligand field arguments are used for very low oxidation states the electrons in the appropriate ion are assigned entirely to d orbitals. For example, a Co^I compound would be regarded as $(3d)^8$ even though the free Co^+ ion has the configuration $(3d)^7 (4s)^1$. The justification for this procedure is that the energy balance between d and s orbitals changes on compound formation; what were s orbitals in the free ion become strongly antibonding molecular orbitals in a complex and are no longer occupied in the ground state.

8.2 Ligand Field Theory

Ligand field splitting of the d orbitals arises from a combination of σ and π bonding interactions with ligands. In octahedral geometry two orbitals (e_s) are at higher energy than the other three (t_{76}). The spectrochemical series puts ligands in order of field strength. High-field ligands are strong σ donors and π acceptors.

Octahedral Splittings

The five d orbitals with different values of the magnetic quantum number (m) have the same energy in a free atom or ion. In any compound, however, they interact differently with the surrounding ligands and a **ligand field splitting** is produced. The commonest coordination is octahedral with six surrounding ligands (see *Fig.* 8.3). Then two of the d orbitals (d_{z2} and d_{x2-y2} known together as the e_g set) are found at higher energy than the other three (d_{xy}, d_{xz} and d_{yz} known as t_{2g}). Such a splitting (denoted Δ_o) occurs in any transition metal compound with octahedral coordination, including aqua ions and many solids. Electronic transitions between t_{2g} and e_g orbitals give rise to colours, which are familiar feature of transition metal complexes, and allow Δ_o to be measured experimentally.

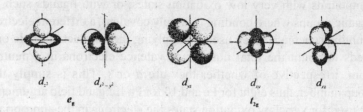

Fig. 8.3. The five d orbitals, showing e_g and t_{2g} sets in an octahedral complex, with ligands among the x, y and z axes.

Although originally explained in terms of electrostatic repulsion between the electrons and the ligands, it is now recognized that ligand field splittings come form the same type of orbital overlap effects as donor-acceptor interactions. Most ligands coordinate to the metal ion using nonbonding electrons. A ligand lone-pair orbital pointing directly towards the metal overlaps with the e_g orbitals (**1**) but has the wrong symmetry to interact with t_{2g}. The overlap gives rise to σ bonding and antibonding molecular orbitals (see *Fig.* 8.2). The bonding orbitals are occupied by the electrons from the ligand, and it is the σ antibonding levels that form the 'metal' e_g set available for the d electrons of the metal ion. A strong σ-donor ligand will produce a large splitting Δ_o by raising the e_g energy. π bonding arises when ligands have orbitals directed perpendicular to the metal-ligand axis, which can interact with the metal t_{2g} orbitals (**2**). Ligands such as halide ions have occupied π orbitals and act as π-donors. This interaction raises the energy of the metal t_{2g} orbitals, and decreases Δ_o. On the other hand; π-**acceptor** ligands such as CO have empty antibonding π orbitals. Overlap with the metal in this case causes the t_{2g} orbitals to be lowered in energy so that Δ_o is increased (see *Fig.* 8.4b and c).

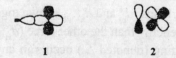

1   **2**

The order of Δ_o values produced by different ligands is known as the spectro-chemical series. A partial series in order of increasing splitting is:

$$I^- < Br^- < Cl^- < F^- < OH^- < H_2O < NH_3 < PPh_3 < CN^- < CO$$

Strong σ donors are generally high in the series, π donors are low and π-acceptor ligands such as CN^- and CO are among the highest. They are known as **strong field ligands**. The major trends with different metal ions are (i) Δ_t increases with charge on the ion, and (ii) splittings are larger for 4d and 5d series elements than in the 3d series.

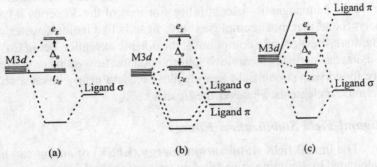

Fig. 8.4. Partial MO diagram showing an octahedral complex with (a) s-donor only, (b) p-donor and (c) p-acceptor ligands.

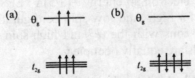

Fig. 8.5. Electron configurations for d^6 in (a) high-spin and (b) low-spin octahedral complex.

High and Low Spin

Assignment of the electron configuration of an octahedral complex involves (i) finding the d electron number of the ion and (ii) determining the occupation of the t_{2g} and e_g orbitals. Electron repulsion effects are important, and other things being equal the ground state will be formed with the maximum number of electrons in different orbitals and with parallel spin. Two and three d electrons occupy the t_{2g} orbitals with parallel spin, but with four or more there are different possibilities. If the extra repulsion coming from **spin-pairing** is large enough, the ground state will be of the **high-spin** type formed by keeping electrons in separate orbitals as far as possible. On the other hand, if Δ_o is larger than the spin-pairing energy, the favoured configuration will be **low-spin** formed by placing as many electrons as possible in t_{2g} even though they must be paired. As shown in *Fig.* 8.5, the high- and low-spin configurations for d^5 are $(t_{2g})^3(e_g)^2$ (five unpaired electrons) and $(t_{2g})^5$ (one unpaired electron), respectively.

The spin state of a transition metal ion can generally be measured from the paramagnetic susceptibility. For ions of the $3d$ series it has been found that most complexes with ligands like halides, water or ammonia are high-spin compounds, the notable exception being Co^{3+}, a d^6 ion that normally forms low-spin compounds. Low-spin complexes are found with strong field ligands like CN^-, and nearly always with $4d$ and $5d$ elements whatever the ligand.

Ligand Field Stabilization Energy

The **ligand field stabilization energy (LFSE)** of an ion can be calculated by summing the orbital energies of the d electrons present, measured relative to the average energy of all five d levels. In octahedral coordination, each electron in a t_{2g} orbital is assigned an energy $-(2/5)\Delta_o$, and each e_g electron an energy $+(3/5)\Delta_o$. LFSE values in terms of Δ_o are shown for high- and low-spin configurations in *Table* 8.1. LFSE is zero for ions with the d^{10} and high-spin d^3 configurations these all d-orbitals are equally occupied.

Table 8.1. Electron configurations for d^n and low-spin octahedral complexes, with corresponding ligand filed stabilization energies

n	High spin		Low spin	
	Configuration	LFSE	Configuration	LFSE
0	–	0	–	–
1	$(t_{2g})^1$	$-2/5\,\Delta_o$	–	–
2	$(t_{2g})^2$	$-4/5\,\Delta_o$	–	–
3	$(t_{2g})^3$	$-6/5\,\Delta_o$	–	–
4	$(t_{2g})^3\,(eg)^{1\,a}$	$-3/5\,\Delta_o$	$(t_{2g})^4$	$-8/5\,\Delta_o$
5	$(t_{2g})^3\,(eg)^2$	0	$(t_{2g})^5$	$-10/5\,\Delta_o$
6	$(t_{2g})^4\,(eg)^2$	$-2/5\,\Delta_o$	$(t_{2g})^6$	$-12/5\,\Delta_o$

| n | High spin | | Low spin | |
---	Configuration	LFSE	Configuration	LFSE
7	$(t_{2g})^5 (eg)^2$	$-4/5 \, \Delta_o$	$(t_{2g})^6 (eg)^{1 \text{ a}}$	$-9/5 \, \Delta_o$
8	$(t_{2g})^6 (eg)^2$	$-6/5 \, \Delta_o$	–	–
9	$(t_{2g})^5 (eg)^{3 \text{ a}}$	$-3/5 \, \Delta_o$	–	–
10	$(t_{2g})^5 (eg)^4$	0	–	–

[a] Configurations susceptible to Jahn-Teller distortion.

Maximum values of octahedral LFSE on high-spin states occur with the d^3 and d^4 configurations, and for low-spin with d^6. These patterns of LFSE influence thermodynamic, structural and kinetic aspects of complex formation. They also have an effect on ionic radii and on lattice and solvation energies. Superimposed on a general decrease of radius along the $3d$ series, the ions with the largest LFSE have smaller radii (and also larger lattice or solvation energies) than otherwise expected. One interpretation of this effect is that in an ion with large LFSE, the repulsion between closed shells is decreased by the predominance of metal electrons in t_{2g} orbitals that do not point directly towards the ligands.

Other Geometries

The pattern of ligand field splitting depends on the coordination geometry generally those d orbitals that point most strongly towards the ligands are raised in energy relative to the others. *Figure* 8.6 shows the splittings produced by some other ligand coordination geometries. **Tetrahedral** coordination gives a splitting in the opposite direction (and about half the magnitude) to that found with octahedral. **Tetragonally distorted octahedral** coordination arises where two opposite ligands are further from the metal than the other four. In this and in **square-planar** coordination, the d orbital pointing towards ligands in the xy plane is higher in energy than the others. (The main difference from the octahedral case is the lowering in energy of d_x, as this interacts less strongly with the ligands).

Ligand field splitting is important in understanding the geometrical preferences of an ion, although other factors may play some part. The splitting in tetrahedral coordination is only about half that for octahedral, and so in competition between octahedral and tetrahedral geometry the octahedral LFSE is more important; thus ions like Cr^{3+} (d^3) and Co^{3+} (d^6 low-spin) are nearly always found in octahedral coordination and are notably resistant to forming tetrahedral complexes. Square-planar complexes are found for d^8 ions when the ligand field splitting is large enough for the electrons to pair in the four lowest orbitals (see *Fig* 8.6); examples are Ni^{2+} with strong-field ligands, and Pd^{2+} and Pt^{2+} in nearly all situations.

The geometry of *Fig.* 8.6 arises from a **Jahn-Teller** distortion of the octahedron. The e_g orbitals are split in energy and this permits stabilization of a complex if these two orbitals are unequally occupied. Thus in d^9 (Cu^{2+}) two electrons occupy the d_{z2} and one the d_{x2-y2}. Nearly all Cu^{2+} compounds show this type of distortion, as do many high-spin d^4 ions such as Cr^{2+}.

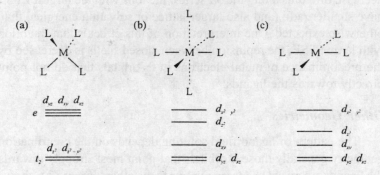

Fig. 8.6. Ligand field splitting patterns for (a) tetrahedral, (b) tetragonally distorted octahedral, and (c) square-planar complexes.

8.3   3d-Series: Aqueous Ions

Oxidation States

Fig. 8.7 shows the **Frost diagram** for the elements of 3d-series (i.e., Sc to Zn). It shows the electrode potentials for aqueous species appropriate to acid solution (pH = 0). In this diagram, the line with *positive slope* indicate that the potential is more *strongly oxidising* and *negative slope* indicate that it is less strongly oxidizing with respect to the standard hydrogen electrode (H^+/H_2)/ the diagram clearly shows the trend that the electropositive character decreases as we move across the series.

It is also quite clear from this diagram that these metals are strong reducing agents (M^{2+}/M or M^{3+}/M couples have negative slope) and the reducing power decreases across the series. The positive slope for Cu^{2+}/Cu indicates that copper metal does not react with acids to give hydrogen. However, copper metal will dissolve in strongly oxidizing acids (*e.g.*, HNO_3) or in the presence of some complexing agent.

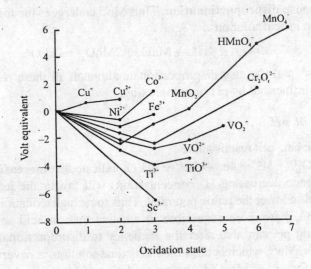

Fig. 8.7. Frost diagram for elements of the 3d series in aqueous solution at pH = 0.

Higher oxidation states are easily accessible for elements early in the series. As far as Mn (group 7), elements can attain the **group oxidation state** (corresponding to the formal d^0 electron configuration). This becomes more oxidizing along the series $Ti^{IV} < V^V < Cr^{VI} < Mn^{VII}$, and permangnate MnO_4^- is used widely as a strong oxidizing agent in acid solution.

M^{2+} ions are stable for all elements except Sc and Ti, where these oxidation states are too strongly reducing to exist in water. M^{3+} ions are formed by elements up to Co, although for Mn and Co the uncomplexed ions are very strongly oxidizing in acid solution. The ionization energy (IE) trend is the most important factor controlling the change in redox stability, and the discontinuity in the trend of third IE values after MN is reflected in a similar break in the M^{3+}/M^{2+} redox potentials, Fe^{3+} being less strongly than MN^{3+}. Changing solvation energies also have an effect, and these are in turn influenced by ligand field stabilization energies (LFSE). The Cr^{3+}/Cr^{2+} couple is more reducing than expected from it third IE as a consequence of the large reduction of lFSE between Cr^{3+} (d^3) and Cr^{2+} (d^t).

Also seen in the diagram is that some intermediate oxidation states are prone to **disproportionation**. Thus Mn^{VI} undergoes the following reaction in acid solution:

$$3MnO_4^{2-} + 4H^+ \rightarrow MnO_2 + 2MnO_4^- + 2H_2O$$

Mn^{3+} and Cu^+ also disproportionate although all these reactions can be influenced by pH or complexing.

Effect of pH

The half-cell reaction like

$FeO_4^{2+} + 8H^+ + 4e^- \rightarrow Fe^{2+} + 4H_2O$, indicate that **increasing pH** (and hence decreasing H^+ concentration) will favour the left-hand side and so lower the redox potential. Thus some high oxidation states like FeO_4^{2-} are more accessible in alkaline than in acid solution. Changing pH can also alter the tendency to disproportionate. For example, Mn^{III}, which is unstable in alkaline solution, is nevertheless readily formed as $Mn(OH)_3$ by air oxidation of $Mn(OH)_2$. Mn^{VI} also resists disproportionation in all alkaline solution.

The species present may change with pH in a way that depends on the oxidation state. Low oxidation states (+2) are always cationic and as pH increases an insoluble hydroxide is eventually precipitated. As the oxidation state increases so does the acidic character of the hydrated cation. Thus M^{3+} ions undergo protolysis even at pH values as low as 1 or 2; deprotonation can be a first step in the formation of oxygen-bridged dimers as with

$$2[Fe(H_2O)_6]^{3+} \rightleftharpoons [(H_2O)_5Fe\text{-}O\text{-}Fe(H_2O)_5]^{4+} + 2H^+$$

These may undergo further polymerization before precipitating as $Fe(OH)_3$.

High oxidation states ($+6$, $+7$) are acidic and always present as anionic species (CrO_4^{2-}, MnO_4^-), although with CrO_4^{2-} dimerization occurs at low pH:

$$2CrO_4^{2-} + 2H + \rightleftharpoons Cr_2O_7^{2-} + H_2O$$

With intermediate oxidation states more complex amphoteric and polymeric behaviour is observed. Thus V^V forms hydrated VO_2^+ in acid solution below pH 2, and the anionic species VO_4^{3+} at high pH. Over an intermediate pH range complex polyvaxadates are formed. The most important is decavanadate ion $[V_{10}O_{28}]^{6-}$ (normally present in protonated forms).

Complex Formation

Complexing behaviour depends on the oxidation state and position in the series, higher oxidation states tend to form stronger complexes with the 'hard' anionic ligands F^- and chelating agents such as EDTA. So we have complexes like $[TiF_6]^{2-}$, $[VF_6]^-$ and $[FeF_6]^{3-}$. Later elements, particularly in low oxidation states, have more affinity for softer ligands like **heavier halides** or ammonia. The stabilities of complexes found with many ligands, particularly ammonia or amines, follow a trend called the **Irving-Williams series:**

$$Mn^{2+} < Fe^{2+} < Co^{2+} < Ni^{2+} < Cu^{2+} > Zn^{2+}$$

Two contributions to this trend are (a) the general decrease in electropositive character resulting from increased effective nuclear charge and (b) ligand field stabilization energies, which increase the stability of complexes field ligands higher in the spectrochemical series than water in all ions except Mn^{2+} (d^5) and Zn^{2+} (d^{10}).

Complexing can have a strong effect on redox chemistry, the general ruke being that a ligand stabilizes whichever oxidation state it complexes with most strongly. Two important examples are:—

(i) Cu^+ forms strong complexes with ligands such as CN^- and I^- so that the Cu^I/Cu potential becomes negative and copper metal will react with acids to form hydrogen; these ligands also stabilize the Cu^I state against disproportionation.

(ii)   Many ligands (*e.g.,* NH_3) complex strongly with Co^{3+}, giving a low-spin a^6 state with a large LFSE. The resulting complexes such as $[Co(NH_3)_6]^{3+}$ are much less strongly oxidizing than aqua Co^{3+} ion, which itself oxidizes water.

Generally negatively charged ligands complex more strongly with ions of higher oxidation state and so reduce the redox potential, whereas neutral π-acceptor ligands, being electron withdrawing, tend to stabilize cations of lower charge and so raise the potential. Ligand field stabilization and other effects cause many complications, however, which can upset these simple generalizations.

8.4   Solid Compounds of 3d-Series

Oxidation States

Compounds are formed with elements in the group oxidation state up to Mn, higher states being found mostly with oxides and fluorides. Lower oxidation states are more stable for later elements. Many mixed-valency and nonstoichiometry compounds are known.

Table 8.2 lists some oxides and halides of 3d-series elements.

Table. 8.2. A selection of oxides and halides of the elements So-Cu. X represents any halogen unless specified. Oxidation states are shown in mixed-valency and ternary compounds.

Element	Oxides	Halides
Sc	Sc_2O_3	Sc_2Cl_3, ScX_3
Ti	TiO_4, Ti_2O_3, $Ti^4_2Ti^{IV}_2O_7$, TiO_2	TiX_2, TiX_3, TiX_4
V	VO_4, V_2O_3, VO_2, V_2O_5	VX_2, VX_3, VX_4, VX_5
Cr	Cr_2O_3, CrO_2, CrO_3, $K_2Cr^{VI}_2O_7$	CrX_2, CrX_3, CrX_4, CrX_5, CrX_6
Mn	MnO, $Mn^{II}Mn^{III}_2O_4$, Mn_2O_3, MnO_2, Mn_2O_7, $KMn^{VII}O_4$	MnX_2, MnF_3, MnF_4
Fe	FeO, $Fe^{II}Fe^{III}_2O_4$, Fe_2O_3, $Sr_2Fe^NO_4$, $K_2Fe^{VI}O_4$	FeX_2, FeX_3 (not I)

Element	Oxides	Halides
Co	CoO, $Co^4Co^{II}_2O_4$, $LaCo^{II}O_3$, $Na_4Co^{IV}O_4$	CoX_2, CoF_3, $Cs_2Co^{IV}F_6$
Ni	NiO, $NaNi^{III}O_2$	NiX_2, $K_2Ni^{IV}F_6$
Cu	Cu_2O, CuO, $LaCu^{II}O_3$	CuX (not F), CuX (not I)
		$K_3Cu^{II}F_6$, $Cs_2Cu^{IV}F_5$

From the table we can see that elements early in series form compounds up to the **group oxidation state**, for example, IIO_2, VF_5 and CrO_3. With increasing group number the higher oxidation states become increasingly hard to form, and can be found only with oxides and/or fluorides, and sometimes only in ternary but not binary compounds. For example, with V^V we can make VF_5 and V_2O_5 but not VCl_5. With Mn^{VII} the only binary compound is Mn_2O_7 but this is much less stable than ternary permanganates such as $KMnO_4$.

The stabilization of high oxidation states by O and F can be attributed at least partly to their small size, which gives the large lattice energies necessary according to the ionic model to compensate for ionization energies. Additional lattice stabilization is possible in ternary structures, as in compounds such as K_2FeO_4 and K_2CoF_6 where no binary compounds with the corresponding oxidation state are stable. It should be recognized that many of the compounds in high oxidation states are not very ionic, and arguments based on the high bond strengths formed by O and F to more electropositive elements may be more satisfactory than using the ionic model.

Low oxidation states (*e.g.*, +2) are of limited stability for the early elements. The unusual **metal-rich** compound Sc_2Cl_3 has 2 structures with extensive Sc-Sc bonds. Compounds such as TiO_r and ViO_r are nonstoichiometric and are also stabilized by metal-metal bonding using d electrons. With Cu the +1 oxidation state is stable in compounds such as Cu_2O and $CuCl$, but CuF is not known, presumably because the larger lattice energy of fluorides makes this unstable with respect to disproportionation to Cu and CuF_2. The differential stability of oxidation states with different halogens is also shown by the existence of CuI but not CuI_2.

The existence of several stable oxidation states gives rise to the possibility of **mixed valency compounds** where an element is present in different oxidation states. Thus the compounds M_3O_4 with M = Mn, Fe, Co, have both M^{II} and M^{III} states present. Many oxides also show **nonstoichiometry** where a continuous range of composition is possible. For example, 'TiO' is really TiO_x where x can vary continuously over a wide range, and 'FeO' does not actually exist but is approximately $Fe_{0.9}O$ (and thermodynamically unstable below 550°C). Such nonstoichiometric compounds are better described by phase diagrams than by simple stoichiometric formulae, which can be misleading.

Halide and Oxide

A majority of halides and oxides have the structures expected for largely ionic compounds, with the metal in **octahedral coordination**. Common oxide structures are rocksalt (*e.g.,* MnOm NiO). Corundum (*e.g.,* Cr_2O_3, Fe2O_3) and rutile (*e.g.,* TiO_2, CrO_2). Most MF_2 compounds have the same rutile structure, other dihalides forming layer ($CdCl_2$ and CdI_2) types. Many ternary oxides and halides also follow this pattern; for example, the $LaMO_3$ compounds formed by all elements of the series (M = Sc–Cu) have the perovskite structure.

The $3d^4$ ions Cr^{2+} and Mn^{3+} and the $3d^9$ ion Cu^{2+} are subject to **Jahn-Teller distortions**. For example, CuO does not have the rocksalt structure, but one with four close Cu–O neighbours and two at longer distance; similar tetragonally distorted coordination is found in most other simple compounds of Cr^{2+} and Cu^{2+}. (Note that CrO is unknown).

Tetrahedral coordination is also sometimes found. In high oxidation states (*e.g.,* molecular $TiCl_4$, polymeric CrO_3 and in complex ions such as VO_4^{3+}, CrO_4^{2-} and MnO_4^{-}) this can be understood in terms of the small size of the transition metal ion. However, tetrahedral (zinc blende) structures are also found in Cu^+ halides such as CuCl. As Cu^+ has the $3d^{10}$ configuration this seems to be typical post-transition metal behaviour as seen, for example, with Zn^{2+}, and must involve some degree of covalent bonding.

Some ternary and mixed-valency oxides have the **spinel structure** where metal ions occupy a proportion of tetrahedral and octahedral holes in a cubic close-packed lattice. Examples include M_3O_4 with M = Mn, Fe, Co. The distribution of M^{2+} and M^{3+} ions between the tetrahedral and octahedral sites shows the influence of ligand field stabilization energies. In Fe_3O_4 Fe^{2+} ($3d^6$) has an octahedral preference whereas Fe^{3+} ($3d^5$) has none, and this compound has the **inverse spinel** structure where Fe^{2+} is octahedral and Fe^{3+} is present in both octahedral and tetrahedral preference and the **normal spinel** structure is found with all Co^{3+} in octahedral sites and Co^{2+} tetrahedral. Mn_3O_4 is also based on the normal spinel structure but with a tetragonal distortion.

Other Binary Compounds

Sulfides are formed by all elements and have structures different from oxides. Many MS compounds (which are generally nonstoichiometric) have the NiAs structure. TiS_2 and VS_2 have layer (CdI_2) structures, but later disulfides contain S_2^{2-} ions (*e.g.*, FeS_2 with the **pyrites** and **marcasite** structures; this is a compound of Fe^{II+} not Fe^{IV}). The compound CuS is particularly complicated, having apparently Cu^+ and Cu^{II} present as well as S^{2-} and S_2^{2-}.

Hydrides, nitride and carbides are known for some of the elements. Some have simple stoichiometry and structure, such as TiN and TiC with the rocksalt structure. Many are nonstoichiometric with metallic properties, and some can be regarded as **interstitial compounds** with the nonmetal atom occupying sites between metallic atoms in the normal elemental structure.

Elements Occurrence and Extraction

The decreasing electropositive character of the elements across the series is shown in the typical minerals they form, and in the methods required to extract them. Early elements are found in oxide or complex oxide minerals (e.g., TiO_2, $CrFeO_3$) and are known as **lithophilic**, whereas later elements are found mainly in sulfides (e.g., NiS) and are called **chalophilic**. Iron forms the dividing line in this trend, and is found both as Fe_2O_3 and FeS_2. Reduction of later elements is relatively easy, as sulphides may roasted to form oxides and then reduced with carbon. For example, iron, a major structural metal, is produced in blast furnaces by reduction of Fe_2O_3:

$$2Fe_2O_3 + 3C \rightarrow 4Fe + 3CO_2$$

However, early transition metal oxides cannot be reduced in this way, because they form stable carbides (e.g., TiC) and/or because the temperature required for reduction by carbon is too high. The **Kroll process** for manufacture of Ti involves first making $TiCl_4$,

$$TiO_2 + 2Cl_2 + 4C \rightarrow TiCl_4 + 4CO$$

which is then reduced by metallic magnesium. Titanium is widely used as a light-weight structural metal; although potentially very reactive towards water and HV it forms a very inert protective TiO_2 film.

8.5 4d-and 5d-Series

Oxidation States

Higher oxidation states are more stable than in the $3d$ series, and lower one less common. The group oxidation state is found up to group 8. $4d$ and $5d$ elements or early groups are very similar; in later groups higher oxidation states occur in the $5d$ series.

Table 8.3 shows the main binary oxides and halides formed by the transition elements of $4d$- and $5d$-series.

Table. 8.3. A selection of oxides and halides of elements from the 4d and 5d series. M represents either of the two elements from the corresponding group, and X any halogen unless exceptions are specified

Element	Oxides	Halides
Y, La	M_2O_3	MX_3
Zr, Hf	MO_2	$ZrCl$, MX_4
Nb, Ta	NbO, MO_2, M_2O_5	M_6X_{14} (not F), MX_3, MX_4, MX_5
Mo, W	MO_2 MO_3, Na_xMO_3	MX_2 (not F), MX_3, MX_4, MoF_5, $MoCl_5$, WX_5 (not I), MoF_6, WF_6, WCl_6
Tc	TcO_2, Tc_2O_7	$TcCl_4$, TcF_5, TcF_6
Re	ReO_2, Re_2O_5, ReO_2, Re_2O_7	Re_3X_9 (not F), ReX_4 (not I), ReX_5 (not I), ReF_6, $ReCl_5$, ReF_7
Ru	RuO_2, RuO_4	RuX_2 (not F), RuX_3, RuF_4, RuF_5, RuF_6

Element	Oxides	Halides
Os	OsO_2, OsO_4	OsX_3 (not F), OsX_4 (not I), OsF_5, $OsCl_5$, OxF_6
Rh	Rh_2O_3, RhO_2	RhX_3, RhF_4, RhF_5, RhF_6
Ir	IrO_2	IrX_3, IrX_4, IrF_4, IrF_5, IrF_6
Pd	PdO	PdX_2, PdF_4
Pt	PtO_2	PtX_2 (not F), PtX_4, PtF_5, PtF_6
Ag	Ag_2O, $Ag^IAg^{II}O_2$	Ag_2, AgX, AgF_2
Au	Au_2O_3	AuX (not F), AuX_3 (not I), AuF_5

The major difference is that the highest oxidation state remains higher than that in $3d$-series, after group 8 *e.g.*, in RuF_6, IrF_6, PtF_6 and AuF_5.

In addition to oxides and halides, high oxidation states are sometimes found with surprising ligands, such as in the ion $[ReH_9]^{2-}$ (1), which is formally a hydride complex of Re^{VII}.

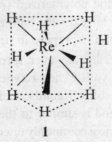

1

A counterpart to the stability of higher oxidation states is that lower ones (+2, +3) are less often found than in the $3d$ series.

For the earlier groups the patterns of $4d$ and $5d$ behaviour are so similar that the corresponding elements (Zr, Hf etc.) are placed together in *Table 8.3*, but in the later groups high oxidation states become slowly less stable in the $4d$ compared with the $5d$ series. This tendency is especially marked with Pd, Pt, Ag and Au. The factors underlying the differences from $3d$ elements, and the general similarity of the two lower series, are discussed in Topic H1. The slow divergence between $4d$ nad $5d$ series arises because increasing nuclear charge across the series has more effect on ionization energies of $4d$ orbitals than on the larger $5d$.

Another trend apparent is the preponderance of oxidation states with even rather than odd electron configurations in later groups; these include Pt^{IV}, Au^V (d^6), (Pd^{II}, Au^{III} (d^8) and Ag^I (d^{10}) is an exception although sometimes the stoichiometry is misleading. AgO being a mixed valency compound $Ag^I AG^{II}O_2$ even electron configurations are favoured by the large ligand field splittings found in these series, giving low spin states, with the d^6 octahedral and d^8 square-planar arrangements being particularly favourable.

Aqueous Chemistry

Unlike elements of the $3d$ series, $4d$ and $5d$ elements have the little simple aqueous cationic chemistry. The main exceptions are Y^{3+} and La^{3+} and Ag^+, which forms some soluble salts (AgF, $AgNO_3$). The aqua Ag^+ ion shows strong class **b** complexing behaviour, with an affinity for ligands such as NH_3, I^- and CN^- comparable with Cd^{2+} in the next group. Some other aqua cations can be made, but they are extensively hydrolyzed and polymerized (*e.g.*, Zr^{4+}, Ht^{4+}), strongly reducing (*e.g.*, Mo^{3+}), or have a very high affinity for other ligands (*e.g.*, Pd^{2+}) and are difficult to prepare in uncomplexed form.

Numerous complexes are, however, formed, the most stable with early groups being ones with F^- and oxygen donor ligands, and in later groups ones with softer ligands such as heavy halides and nitrogen donors. This trend is similar to that found in the $3d$ series but is more marked. The most commonly encountered solution species for later elements are chloride complexes such as $[PdCl_4]^{2-}$, $[PiCl_6]^{4-}$ and $[AuCl_4]^-$.

Oxanions are formed by elements of groups 5-8, examples being MoO_4^{2-}, ReO_4^- and RuO_4^{2-}. They are invariably less strongly oxidizing than their counterparts in the $3d$ series. Mo^{VI} and W^{VI}, and to a lesser extent Nb^V and Ta^V, form extensive series of polymeric oxoanions: **isopolymetallates** such as $[Mo_6O_{19}]^{2-}$ and $[Ta_6O_{19}]^{3-}$ are mostly based on metal oxygen octahedra sharing corners and edges; **heteropolymetallates** like the phosphopolymolybdate ion $[PMo_{12}O_{40}]^{3-}$ incorporate other elements, in this case as a tetrahedral PO_4 group.

Solid Structures

Larger ionic radii compared with the $3d$ series elements often lead to higher coordination numbers ZrO_2 and HfO_2 can adopt the eight coordinated fluorite as well as 2 unique seven coordinate structure called baddeleyite (*e.g.* TiO_2, rutile). ReO_3 is the prototype of a structure with six coordination, and is adopted also (in slightly distorted form) by WO_3, in contrasts to Cr^{VI}, which is tetrahedral. MoO_3 and WO_3 form extensive series of insertion compounds called **oxide bronzes**. In halides, higher coordination often leads to polymeric forms for compounds MX_4 and MX_5 where the corresponding $3d$ compounds are molecular.

Compounds of elements in low oxidation states very frequently have extensive **metal-metal bonding**. Sometimes this acts to modify an otherwise normal structure, as in NbO_2, MoO_2 and WO_2, which have the rutile form distorted by the formation of pairs of metal atoms. Often the structures are unique. For example, $MoCl_2$ contains $[Mo_6Cl_8]^{4+}$ clusters formed by metal-metal bonded octahedra with chlorine in the face positions (see **2**; only one of eight Cl shown). Complex halides often show metal-metal bonding, such as in $[Re_2Cl_5]^{2-}$ (**3**) where all four d electrons of Re^{III} are paired to form a quadruple bond.

2	**3**

Later elements tend to show coordination geometries that are specific to certain low-spin electron configurations. d^6 compounds are invariably octahedral, d^8 nearly always square planar (e.g., in $PdCl_2$ **4** and PdO; a rare exception is PdF_2, which, like NiF_2, has the octahedral rutile structure with two unpaired electrons per Pd). The d^{10} configuration often has a tendency to linear two-coordination (cf. Hg^{II}). Although AgF, AgCl and AgBr have the rocksalt structure some other Ag^1 compounds such as Ag_2O have two-coordination, and it is normal for Au^1; for example, $AuCl$ has a chain structure with a linear Cl-Au-Cl arrangement.

4

8.6 Complexes of Transition Metals (Structure and Isomerism)

Coordination Number and Geometry

Coordination and geometry are determined by *size* and *bonding factors*.

Transition metal complexes are cationic, neutral or anionic species in which a transition metal is coordinated by ligands. A **classical** or **Werner complex** is one formed by 2 metal in a positive oxidation state with donor ligands such as H_2O, NH_3, or halide ions.

The **coordination numbers** (CN) observed in complexes range from two (*e.g.,* $[Ag(NH_3)_2]^+$) to nine (e.g., $[ReH_9]^{2-}$. The commonest geometries for $3d$ ions are **octahedral** (CN = 6, *e.g.,* $[M(H_2O)_6]^{2+}$) and **tetrahedral** (CN = 4, *e.g,* $[MCl_4]^{2-}$). As in solid compounds, higher coordination numbers are often found with the larger $4d$ and $5d$ ions. Other coordination geometries may be dictated by bonding arrangements depending on the d electron number.

The relative preference for octahedral or tetrahedral coordination is partly steric, but ligand field effects can also play a role. Ions with the d^3 and low-spin d^6 configurations (*e.g,* Cr^{3+} and Co^{3+}, respectively) have a large octahedral ligand field stabilization energy and are notably resistant to forming tetrahedral complexes. **Square-planar** complexes would never be predicted in preference to tetrahedra on steric grounds alone. They are commonly found, however, with $4d^6$ and $5d^8$ ions such as Pd^{2+} and Pt^{2+} where the pattern of ligand field splitting is favourable if its magnitude is large enough for spin-pairing to occur. The corresponding $3d^6$ and Ni^{2+} gives square-planar complexes only with strong-field ligands such as CN^-, otherwise octahedral or sometimes tetrahedral coordination is found. With the d^9 or high-spin d^4 configuration a distorted octahedral geometry is often found with only four ligands strongly attached. This is common with Cu^{2+}, as in $[Cu(NH_3)_4]^{2+}$, where two weakly bound water molecules are also present.

Low coordination numbers are often found with post-transition metal ions having the d^{10} configuration. This is also true for the d^{10} ions Cu^+, Ag^+ and Au^+, which form many linear complexes with CN = 2 (*e.g.*, $[AuCl_2]^-$, isoelectronic to $HgCl_2$).

Polynuclear complexes contain more than one metal atom. Sometimes these may be held by bridging ligands, as in $[(RuCl_5)_2O]^{4-}$ **(1)**. In other cases **metal-metal bonds** may be present, as in $[Re_2Cl_3]^{2-}$. Metal-metal bonding is common in $4d$- and $5d$-series than in the $3d$-elements, although binuclear compounds of Cr^{II} are known; for example, $[Cr_2(CH_3CO_2)_4]$ **(2)**, which has bridging acetate groups (only one shown explicitly) and a quadruple Cr–Cr bond formed by all remaining valence electrons of the $3d^4$ ions.

1   **2**

Nomenclature

The naming of coordination compounds is illustrated examples that will illustrate the principles involved.

(i) $[Ni(H_2O_8)^{2+}$, hexaaquanickel(II) ion; $[Cu(NH_3)_4]^{2+}$ tetraamminecopper(II) ion. The terms **aqua** and **ammine** are used for water and ammonia ligands. Other neutral ligands are referred to by their normal (molecular) name. Sometimes the prefixes **bis, tris,** ... are used where normal form (bi, tri...) could cause confusion with the ligand name; for example, $[Co(H_2O)_3(CH_3NH_2)_3]^{3+}$, tris(methylamine) triaquacobalt(III) ion.

(ii) $[CoCl_4]^{2-}$ tetrachlorocobaltate(II), $[Fe(CN)_6]^{3-}$ hexacyanoferrate(3-). For anionic ligands the normal ending – ide is replaced by –o. manes of anionic complexes end in –ate, and are sometimes based on Latin rather than English names of the metallic element. Either the oxidation state of the metal atom or the total charge on the complex is specified.

(iii) $[CoCl(NH_3)_5]Cl_2$, pentaamminechlorocobalt(III) chloride. Coordinated ligands are shown in square brackets, others are assumed to be separate in the structure. Anionic ligands are usually written before neutral ones in the formula, but after them in the name.

(iv) $[(RuCl_5)_2O]^{4-}$ **(1)**, m-oxo-bis(pentachlororuthenate)(4-). The Greek letter u ('mu') is used to denote bridging ligands.

Isomerism

Isomers are compounds with the (molecular) formula but different structure. When several isomers exist one or may be thermodynamically more stable than others, or then may be an equilibrium between them. Thus the isolation study of individual isomer depends on kinetic factors that limit the rate of interconversion. Such kinetic inertness is associated with only a few ions and most examples of isomerism involve complexes of Cr^{3+}, Co^{2+} and Pt^{2+}.

Ionism Isomerism

This is shown by an example. $CrCl_3$, $6H_2O$ exists in four solid forms, which dissolve in water to give different species.

$[Cr(H_2O)_6Cl]_3 \rightarrow [Cr(H_2O_6)]^{3+} + 3Cl^-$

$[Cr(H_2O)_5Cl]Cl_2H_2O \rightarrow [Cr(H_2O)_5Cl]^{2+} + 2Cl^- + H_2O$

$[Cr(H_2O)_4Cl_2]Cl.2H_2O \rightarrow [Cr(H_2O)_4Cl_2]^+ + Cl^- + 2H_2O$

$[Cr(H_2O)_3Cl_3]\,3H_2O \rightarrow [Cr(H_2O)_3Cl_3] + 3H_2O$

The different isomers contain an octahedral Cr^{III} complex but the coordinated ligands are different; for example, in the first case the three Cl^- ions are present in the crystal lattice of the solid compounds but are not directly bound to the metal.

Linkage Isomers

A few ligands are ambiotenate, measure that they can coordinate through alternative ligand atoms. Examples are nitric NO_2^- (which an bind through N or O) and SCN^- (S or N.) the nomenclature **N-nitrito** is recommended for complexes where in formulae the ligand atom is underlined, $M–NO_2$ and $M–ONO$, respectively (although the nonsystematic names **nitro** and nitrate also used for NO_2^- complexes.

Geometrical Isomerisms

The fact that a tetrahedrally coordinate compound MX_2Y_2 has only one possible isomer was historically important in establishing the structure of carbon compounds. When the coordination is **square-planar** there are two possibilities, known as the *cis* (3) and *trans* (4) forms. Geometrical isomers occur also in octahedral complexes with MX_2Y_4 the two isomers are also called *cis* (5) and *trans* (6) and for MX_3Y_3 the terms *mer* (7) and *fac* (8 from 'facial') are used.

$$
\begin{array}{ccc}
\begin{matrix} X \\ | \\ X-M-Y \\ | \\ Y \end{matrix}
&
\begin{matrix} X \\ | \\ Y-M-Y \\ | \\ X \end{matrix}
&
\begin{matrix} X \quad Y \\ | \nearrow \\ X-M-Y \\ \swarrow | \\ X \quad Y \end{matrix}
\\
\mathbf{3} & \mathbf{4} & \mathbf{5}
\end{array}
$$

$$
\begin{array}{ccc}
\begin{matrix} X \quad Y \\ | \nearrow \\ X-M-X \\ \swarrow | \\ Y \quad X \end{matrix}
&
\begin{matrix} X \quad Y \\ | \nearrow \\ X-M-X \\ \swarrow | \\ Y \quad Y \end{matrix}
&
\begin{matrix} X \quad X \\ | \nearrow \\ X-M-Y \\ \swarrow | \\ Y \quad Y \end{matrix}
\\
\mathbf{6} & \mathbf{7} & \mathbf{8}
\end{array}
$$

Geometrical isomerism can also refer to the possibility of different coordination geometries, although these are rather rare. Square-planar or tetrahedral coordination is, in principle, possible with CN = 4, and an example with CN = 5 occurs with $[Ni(CN)_5]^{3-}$, which can adopt shapes approximating either to a trigonal bypyramid (the normally expected shape; see Topic C2) or a square pyramid (9).

9   10   11

Optical Isomerism

When a species cannot be superimposed on its minor image the two forms are known as **enantiomers or optical isomers.** Most examples with coordination compounds have chelating (*e.g.,* bidentate) ligands. Structures **10** and **11** show respectively the *delta* and *lambda* isomers of a tris(chelate) complex, with the bidentate ligands each denoted by a simple bond framework.

8.7   Kinetics and Mechanism of Complexes of Transition Metals

Ligand Exchange

Ligand exchange mechanism may be associative (A), dissociative (D) or Interchange (I_a or I_d). Kinetically inert complexes are formed by Cr^{3+} and Co^{3+} and by 4d- and 5d-ions with d^6 and d^8 configuration.

Ligand exchange reactions are of the kind

$$ML\pi X + Y \rightarrow ML\pi Y + X$$

Which are **nucleophillic substitutions.** Kinetic studies of ligand exchange can sometimes distinguish between the mechanisms although these results can be misleading. Determination of the volume or entropy of activation (*i.e.,* the volume or entropy change in the transition state) can often give guidance.

For many metal ions ligand exchange is an extremely fast reaction, with rate constants close to the limit of diffusion control (around 10^{10} $M^{-1}\ s^{-1}$ in water). There is a correlation with the charge and size, and outside the transition series Be^{2+} and Al^{3+}, which have large charge/ size ratio, have significantly slower exchange. With transition metals the influence of ligands field affects is apparent (see Topic H2). Complexes of Cr^{3+} (d^3) and Co^{3+} (d^6) and of many d^6 and d^8 ions in the 4d and 5d series are **kinetically inert** and undergoes ligand substitution many orders of magnitude more slowly than comparable nontransition ions. These ions have a ligand field stabilization energy (LPSE) that contributes a barrier to the geometrical change required in the transition state. A large LPSE value also gives shorter bond lengths, which enhance other contributions (electrostatic, etc.) to the metal-ligand bond strength.

The existence of kinetically inert complexes is useful in mechanistic studies, and important for the separation of different isomers.

Octahedral Complexes

Most M^{2+} ions of the 3d series undergo ligand exchange at a rate comparable with that for nontransition metal ions of similar size. V^{2+} (d^3) and Ni^{2+} (d^8) are somewhat slower, these being the electron configurations that give maximum octahedral LFSE for high-spin ions. Entropies and volumes of activation suggest a change from predominantly I_6 mechanisms early in the series (e.g., V^{2+}) to I_4 towards the end (e.g, Ni^{2+}). Both decreasing size and increasing d orbital occupancy may contribute to this trend. Incoming ligands in the I_4 mechanism must approach an octahedral complex along directions where the t_{2g} obtains normally point. Filling these orbitals will tend to inhibit the approach of ligands and favour the dissociative pathway.

For the kinetically inert low-spin Co^{III} complexes the mechanism of exchange is certainly dissociative although kinetic studies can give results that are superficially misleading. For example, the base hydrolysis reaction

$$[Co(NH_3)_5Cl]^{2+} + OH^- \rightarrow [Co(NH_3)_5OH]^{2+} + Cl^-$$

has a rate proportional to the concentrations of both complex and OH⁻. This is not indicative of an associative mechanism, but of a **conjugate base mechanism** where the first reversible step is deprotonation of the complex:

$$[Co(NH_3)_5Cl]^{2+} + OH^- \rightleftharpoons [Co(NH_3)_4(NH_2)Cl]^+ + H_2O$$

Deprotonation *trans* to the leaving group is especially effective at promoting the dissociation step. The conjugate base mechanism cannot operate if a tertiary amine with no ionizable proton is placed *trans* to the leaving group; as expected the rate of substitution is then slower and does not depend on [OH⁻].

Square-planar Complexes

Kinetically inert square-planar complexes are found by d^8 low-spin ions, particularly Pt^{2+}. Ligand substitution is associative and correlated with the ease of forming a five coordinate transition state (or intermediate). Substitution is much faster with Ni^{2+} where five-coordinate complexes such as $[Ni(CN)_5]^{3-}$ are more stable than for Pt. For a given metal, the rate of substitution is controlled by:

(i)   the nature of the incoming and leaving ligands; more polarizable groups are generally faster in both bond-making and breaking processes;

(ii) the *trans effect*, which is *the ability of some ligands to facilitate the substitution of the ligand trans to them in the complex.* Some ligands in order of increasing effectiveness are given below:

$$NH_3 < Cl^- < Br^- < H^-, PR_3 < CN^-, CO$$

The *trans effect* is a **kinetic phenomenon** and is influenced by different factors that operate either in the ground state or in the five-coordinate transition state. Some ligands weaken the bond *trans* to them in the original complex. This ground-state phenomenon is known as the *trans* **influence**, and depends mostly on the σ bonding capability and the polarizability of the ligand. Some ligands such as CN⁻ do not show much *trans* influence but nevertheless have a large kinetic *trans* effect, because their π-acceptor properties help in the stabilization of the transition state.

The *trans* effect is useful in synthesis. For example, different isomers are formed in the reactions below by the greater *trans* directing ability of Cl⁻ compared, with NH_3:

$$[Pt(NH_3)Cl_3]^- + NH_3 \rightarrow cis\text{-}[Pt(NH_3)_2Cl_2] + Cl^-$$
$$[Pt(NH_5)_3Cl]^+ + Cl^- \rightarrow trans\text{-}[Pt(NH_3)_2Cl_2] + NH_3$$

Electron Transfer Reactions

Electron transfer is the simplest type of redox process, for example

$$V^{2+} + Fe^{3+} \rightarrow V^{3+} + Fe^{2+}$$

A majority of reactions of this type are very fast, but oxidation by some complexes (especially of Co^{III}) is much slower.

In an **inner sphere** process, the coordination sphere of one complex is substitute by a ligand bound to the other complex which then acts as a bridge and may be transferred during the redox process. For example, isotopic labeling studies show that to oxidation of aqueous Cr^{2+} with $[Co^{III}(NH_3)_5Cl]^{2+}$ proceeds via a bridges species Cr–Cl–Co, the chlorine not exchanging with free labeled Cl⁻ in solution but remaining attached to the kinetically inert Cr^{III} product. An inner sphere mechanism requires one of the reactants to be substitutionally labile, and a ligand that can act as a bridge. One test is to compare the rates of reaction with the ligands azide N_3^- and (N bonded) thiocynanate NCS⁻; azide is generally better at bridging and so gives faster if the inner sphere route is operating.

The **outer sphere** mechanism involves no disruption of the coordination of either complex, and is always available as a route to electron transfer unless the inner sphere rate is faster. The **Marcus theory** shows that the rate of outer sphere transfer depends on the following:

(i) The orbital interaction between the two metal centres involved, a factor that decreases roughly exponentially with the distance between them;

(ii) The change in metal-ligand distances resulting from electron transfer, the effect that provides most of the activation energy for the reaction;

(iii)   An enhancement term, which depends on the difference of redox potentials of the two couples involved.

Reactions of complexes containing unsaturated ligands such as bipyridyl are generally fast because the π system facilitates transfer, and because the change in geometry is small (as significant charge is distributed over the ligand). On the other hand, oxidation by $[Co(NH_3)_6]^{3+}$ is often very slow. The orbital interaction terms is small because the reaction is 'spin forbidden', the ground state of Co changing from low-spin d^6 with no unpaired electrons to high-spin Co^{2+} d^7 with three. The activation energy is also large because the number of e_g electrons increases by two, which gives a significant change of LFSE and so causes a large increase in the metal-ligands distances. The inner sphere route is unavailable as NH_3 does not normally act as a bridging ligand.

8.8   Electronic Spectra and Magnetic Properties of Complexes of Transition Metals

Electronic Transitions

In an electronic transition an electron is excited from an occupied to an empty molecular orbital (MO). The energy of such transitions normally corresponds to photons in the near IR, visible or UV region of the electromagnetic spectrum. Electronic **absorption bands** give rise to the colours of compounds, including ones without transition metals.

In d-blocks complexes different types of MO can be involved. In d-d transitions both the lower and upper MOs are those based on the d atomic orbitals, split by interaction with ligands. **Charge transfer transitions** involve ligand-based MOs as well, and may be divided intro **ligands-to-metal charge transfer** (LMCT, the commonest type) or **metal-to-ligand charge transfer** (MLCT). There may also be transitions between two ligand MOs (e.g. π to π* in unsaturated ligands). Charge transfer and ligand-based transition generally appear at higher energy that d-d transitions, and are generally also more intense. Figure 8.8 shows the absorption spectrum of $[Ti(H_2O)_6]^{3+}$. The d–d transition peaks at around 20 000 cm^{-1}·(500 nm) corresponding to green light, giving a violet colour to the complex (transmitting red and violet light). The strong absorption rising beyond $25\ 000\ cm^{-1}$ is due to LMCT.

d–d Spectra

d–d transitions are weak due to atomic **selection rules**, that make transitions between *d* orbitals **forbidden**. They remain forbidden in complexes with a centre of symmetry (*e.g.* octahedral or square planar), and appear only because of vibrational motions that break this symmetry. In complexes without a centre of symmetry (*e.g.* tetrahedral) the transitions are stronger but are still weak compared with charge transfer. There are also spin selection rules, the strongest transitions being **spin-allowed** ones where there is no change in the number of unpaired electrons.

In a d^1 octahedral complex like $[Ti(H_2O)_6]^{3+}$ excitation of an electron from t_{2g} to e_g gives a single absorption band at an energy equal to the ligand field splitting Δ_o. The theory is more complicated for ions with many *d* electrons because the energy of a state is now determined by the repulsion between electrons as well as the occupancy of t_{2g} and e_g orbitals. The predicted number of spin-allowed *d–d* transitions in high-spin octahedral or tetrahedral complexes is shown below. Not all transition may be visible in all cases, because bands may overlap or some may be obscured by charge transfer:

one for d^1, d^4, d^6 and d^9;
three for d^2, d^3, d^7 and d^8;
none for d^0, d^5 and d^{10}.

The absence of spin-allowed transitions for high-spin d^5 can be understood from the fact that in ground state all *d* orbitals are singly occupied by electrons having parallel spin. This is the only possible state with five unpaired electrons, and any *d–d* transitions must involve a change of spin. *d–d* transitions in high-spin Mn^{2+} and Fe^{3+} complexes are indeed very weak compared with other ions, which have spin-allowed transitions.

A mathematical analysis of the transition energies in d^n ions allows Δ_o to be determined as well as **electron repulsion parameters**. Electron repulsion between *d* electrons in complexes is found to be less than in the free gas-phase d^n ions. This reduction is called the **nephelauxetic effect** (meaning 'cloud expanding') and arises because 'd orbitals' in complexes are really MOs with some ligand as also metal contribution, so the electron are on average further apart than in the pure d orbitals of the uncombined ions. Larger nephelauxetic reductions are observed in complexes with 'soft' ligands such as I⁻ than with 'hard' ones such F⁻, reflecting the greater degree of covalent bonding in the former case.

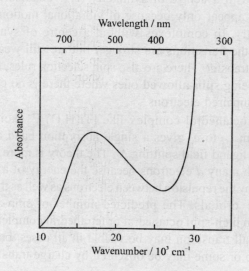

Fig. 8.8. Absorption spectrum of $[Ti(H_2O)_6]^{3+}$.

Charge Transfer Spectra

Charge transfer is similar to an **internal redox reaction,** and the absorption energies can be correlated with trends in redox properties. In LMCT an electron is transferred to the metal, which is therefore reduced in the excited state. The more positive the redox potential concerned, the easier such reduction will be, and so the lower the LMCT energy. LMCT transitions in the visible region of the spectrum give intense colour, as is found with permangnate MnO_4^-, a d⁰ complex, which therefore has no d-d transitions. The energy trends in some of d^0 species are:

(i) $MnO_4 < CrO_4^{2-} < VO_4^{3-}$;

(ii) $MnO_4^- < TcO_4^- < ReO_4^-$;

which follow the trends towards less strongly oxidizing compounds, (i) towards the left in the $3d$ series and (ii) down each transition metal group. The above orders of LMCT energy are reflected in the changing colours of the ions (*e.g.,* MnO_4^- deep purple, CrO_4^{2-} deep yellow, VO_4^{3-} pale yellow, as the transition moves progressively to higher energy out of the visible spectrum into the UV).

LMCT energies also follow expected trends as the ligand is changed, for example, O > S, and F > CL > Br, as the heavier ions in each group are more easily oxidized. With different metal ions, there is a general decrease in energy towards the right in each series. For ions in lower oxidation states, LMCT often occurs in the UV rather than the visible part of the spectrum.

MLCT is less common, as it requires the extensive of empty ligand orbitals of suitable energy. Many of these ligands are π acceptors. With changing metal ions and oxidation states, MLCT bands often follow the reverse of the trends found with LMCT.

Paramagnetism

In **diamagnetism** substances are repelled by a magnetic field: this property is associated with all *closed electron shells*. **Paramagnetic** substances are attached into a magnetic field, the force being related to the **magnetic susceptibility**. Paramagnetism normally arises from the spin of **unpaired electrons**. The Curie law for the susceptibility per mole (χ_m) is

$$\chi_m = \frac{N_A \mu_0 \mu_{eff}^2}{3kT}$$

where N_A is Avogadro's number, μ_0 the magnetic permeability of free space, μ_{eff} the **effective magnetic moment** of the paramagnetic species, k is Boltzmann's constant and T the temperature in Kelvin. The inverse temperature dependence arises as thermal agitation acts against the alignment of moments in an applied field. For many d-block compounds the **spin-only formula** is a fairly good approximation to the effective magnetic moment:

$$\mu_{eff} = 2[S \ (S + 1)^{1/4}\mu_g = [n(n + 2)^{1/4}\mu_g,$$

where S is the spin quantum number, equal to half the number of unpaired electrons n, and μ_g the **Bohr magneton**, equal to approximately 9.274×10^{-24} JT^{-1}. The most straightforward application of magnetic measurements therefore is to establish the number of unpaired electrons, and so as to distinguish between high and low-spin states. For example, most Co^{3-} complexes have $\mu_{eff} = 0$ as expected for low-spin d^6; however, $[CoF_6]^{3-}$ has μ_{eff} around $5\mu_g$, corresponding to four unpaired electrons and a high-spin state.

Magnetic measurements are sometimes used to give information about **metal-metal** bonding. For example, dimeric Cr^{2+} complexes such as $[Cr_2(CH_3CO_2)_4]$ have $\mu_{eff} = 0$, suggesting that all four electrons of Cr^{2+} are paired to form a quadruple bond. However, there are many other factors that can complicate magnetic properties. The oxygen-bridged complex $[(RuCl_5)_2O]^{4-}$ also has $\mu_{eff} = 0$. in this case, there is no metal-metal bond and the electrons are based as a consequence of the Ru-CL bonding.

8.9 π-Acceptor Ligand Complexes Formed by Transition Metals

Introduction

Most ligands have a nonbonding electron pair that can act as a donor to empty orbitals on the metal atom. In ligands called π-**acceptors** or π **acids** a donor-acceptor interaction also occur in the reverse direction. If a ligand has empty orbitals of π type symmetry with respect to the bond axis these must act as acceptors for electrons in filled metal orbitals of the correct symmetry. This is shown as **back donation**. The simplest and commonest π acid ligand is carbon monoxide CO. This acts as a σ donor in the normal way, through the occupied lone-pair orbital centred on carbon. The π antibonding orbital can also interact with filled d orbitals to give the π-acceptor interaction (*Fig.* 8.9). The combination of σ-donor and π-acceptor interaction is sometimes described as **synergic**, as the electron flows in opposite directions facilitate each other.

Evidence for the π-acceptor interaction comes from different sources.

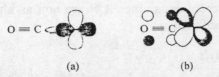

Fig. 8.7. Bonding in CO complexes showing (a) s overlap of CO lone-pair with empty metal d orbital, and (b) overlap of CO p* with occupied metal of orbital.

(i) CO and related ligands stabilize **very low oxidation states** of transition elements, often zero. p-acceptor interactions remove electron density from a metal atom and make possible a lower oxidation state than is commonly found with ligands like water and ammonia.

(ii) Partial occupation of the π antibonding orbital in CO weakens the bond. This is most easily seen from the **bond stretching frequency** measured by IR spectroscopy. CO stretching frequencies in carbonyl compounds are nearly always less than in free CO, and also decrease in a sequence such as

$$[Mn(CO)_6]^+ > [Cr(CO)_6] > [V(CO)_6]^-$$

where the availability of metal electrons for back donation is increasing. (A few CO complexes *e.g.*, BH_3CO and $Au(Cl)CO$ have stretching frequency slightly higher than in the free molecule indicating that little or no π interaction is occurs in these cases.

π-acceptor properties in other ligands may be judged by their ability to stabilize low oxidation states in a similar way to CO, or by their effect on the CO stretching frequency when placed in the same complex. Two π-acceptor ligands in a *trans* configuration will complete for the same d orbitals. Placing a strong π acceptor *trans* to CO will therefore lessen the availability if electrons for back-bonding and so the CO stretching frequency will be higher than otherwise. On the basis the following **order of π-acceptor strength** has been deduced for some ligands:

$$NO > CO > RNC > PF_3 > P(OR)_3 > PR_3 > RCN > NR_3$$

π back-bonding with phosphines is generally assumed to involve valence expansion on the phosphorous. As expected, the strength increases with the electronegativity of the attached groups. Although nitrogen ligands such as pyridine (where N is part of an aromatic ring system) are π acceptors, amines R_3N are not, as nitrogen cannot expand it's valence shell.

Binary Carbonyls

CO forms binary neutral compounds with most transition metals, and some anionic and cationic species. *Table* 8.4 shows compounds from the 3*d* series. Some of these compounds can be obtained by direct reaction of the metal and CO at high pressure. The **Mond process** for the purification of nickel depends on the formation of nickel tetra-carbonyl $Ni(CO)_4$ in this way, followed by its thermal decomposition to deposit metallic nickel. For earlier elements in the series **reductive carbonylation** is required, with a compound (generally a halide) reduced in the presence of CO at high pressure. Polynuclear carbonyls are formed naturally for some elements (Mn, Co); in other cases, such as Fe where the mononuclear carbonyl $Fe(CO)_5$ is stable, polynuclear compounds can be made from it by photolysis or controlled pyrolysis. Binary carbonyls are volatile compounds, often very toxic, and thermodynamically not stable in the presence of oxygen but often with considerable kinetic stability, especially for metals later on the series.

Table 8.4. Binary carbonyls and ions formed by 3d series elements

$V(CO)_6$	$Cr(CO)_6$	$Mn_2(CO)_{10}$	$Fe(CO)_5$	$Co_2(CO)_8$	$Ni(CO)_4$
$[V(CO)_6]^-$		$[Mn(CO)_5]^+$	$[Fe(CO)_4]^{2-}$	$[Co_2(CO)_4]^-$	
			$Fe_2(CO)_9$		
			$Fe_3(CO)_{12}$		

In mononuclear carbonyls CO is invariably attached to the metal through carbon giving a linear M-C-O arrangement. Polynuclear carbonyls have relatively short distances between metal atoms indicative of **metal-metal bonds**. CO can then bond on either a **terminal** or a **bridging** mode, the former bonded to one metals as in $Mn_2(CO)_{10}$ **(1)** and the latter attached to more than one metals as in $Co_2(CO)_8$ **(2)**. In larger clusters formed by some elements, triply bridging CO is also possible. Terminal and bridging CO may be distinguished by IR spectroscopy, as bridging groups show a characteristically lower stretching frequency.

1

2

Many compounds are known containing CO in conjunction with other ligands, which may include π acceptors such as phosphines, and/or σ bonding ligands. For example, there is a series of compounds $Mn(CO)_5X$, where X = H, halogen or an alkyl group.

The 18-electron Rule

A large number of stable carbonyls obey the **18-electron rule** (sometimes known as the **effective atomic number (EAN) rule**. To use this rule one first counts the number of valence electrons in the neutral atom, equal to the group number (thus both s and d electrons are included; then adds two electrons for the lone-pair of each attached CO. For example, in $Fe(CO)_5$, the group number of Fe is eight; five COs make 18. The EAN calculation starts with the actual atomic number (Fe = 26). Adding two electrons for each CO makes an EAN = 36, which is the noble gas configuration of Kr. The only difference between the 18-electron and the EAN count is that the latter includes core electrons and so gives a different count for the three series: 36 (Kr core) for $3d$, 54 (Xe core) for $4d$ and 86 (Ra core) for $5d$.

All the mononuclear species effect $V(Co)_6$ in Table 8.4 satisfy the 18-electron rule. The bi- and tri-nuclear species do also if (i) the two electrons in a metal-metal bond are counted as contributing to the valence shells of both metal atoms concerned, and (ii) a bridging CO contributes one electron to each metal. Monomeric Mn and Co carbonyls would have an odd number of electrons and dimerize in consequence. $V(CO)_6$ is exceptional as a stable radical with 17 valence-shell electrons, presumably because it is satirically impossible for it to dimerize without losing one CO ligand. It does, however, readily form the 18-electron anion $[V(CO)_6]^-$.

When other ligands are present it is normal in 18-electron counting to assume covalent rather than ionic bonding. In $Mn(CO)_5X$, where $X = H$, Cl or CH_3, Mn and X therefore contribute one electron each to the Mn–X bond, and X is regarded as a one-electron ligand even if it is a halogen.

One can make a connection between the 18-electron rule and ligand field theory but noting that a d^6 octahedral complex has 18 valence electrons. π-acceptor ligands provide strong fields and hence low-spin configurations thus making the d^6 octahedral combination extremely favourable. In general, the 18-electron configuration with π-acceptor ligands provide a large gap between the highest occupied MO (HOMO) and the lowest unoccupied MO (LUMO). Without the stabilization of the lower-energy set of d orbitals provided by a π-acceptor ligand the HOMO-LUMO gap is not so large, and the 18-electron rule does not generally apply to complexes with weak-field ligands. Even with π-acceptor ligands it can break down under some circumstances. For example

(i) With elements early in the transition series that contribute few electrons themselves it may be sterically impossible to coordinate enough ligands to achieve the 18-electron count. $V(CO)_6$ is an example.

(ii) For later elements (group 9 onwards) there is a tendency towards lower electron counts (see below).

16-electron Complexes

A square-planar complex of d^8 ion, such as $[Ni(CN)_4]^{2-}$, has a valence electron count of 16 and not 18 similar **16-electron complexes** are formed by other elements in group 9, 10 and 11, for example **Vaska's** compound $Ir[(CO)(PPh_3)_2Cl$ **(3)**. Some 16-electron complexes (especilaly in the $3d$ series) can readily add another ligand to form a five-coordinate 18-electron complex such as $[Ni(CN)_5]^{3-}$. Another important reaction is known as **oxidative** addition, where a molecule X–Y adds by cleavage of the bond to form an 18-electron complex that can considered as d^6 octahedral:

$$Ir^I(CO)(PPh_3)_2Cl + X-Y \rightarrow Ir^{III}(CO)(PPh_3)_2(X)(Y)Cl$$

X–Y can be a simple molecule such as H_2 or HCl, or an organic compound. Vaska's compound also reacts with O_2 to form $Ir(CO)(PPh_3)_2(O_2)$ (**4**). In this case, O_2 remains intact on coordination, although the bond lengthens, suggesting that **4** can be considered as a complex with a bidentate peroxo ligand. (O_2^{2-})

$$Ph_3P \longrightarrow \underset{\underset{Cl}{|}}{\overset{\overset{CO}{|}}{Ir}} \longrightarrow PPh_3$$

3

$$\underset{Ph_3P}{\overset{OC}{\underset{Cl}{\diagdown}}} \overset{PPh_3}{\underset{\diagup}{\overset{|}{Ir}}} \overset{O}{\underset{O}{\diagdown}}$$

4

The reverse of oxidative addition is reductive elimination. Such reversible processes are important in many catalytic cycles involving transition metal compounds.

8.10 Organometallic Compounds of Transition Metals

Organic ligands for transition metals are classified by their hapticity (the number of bonded atoms) and by the number of electrons they provide in bonding. Sometimes but not always these numbers are equal.

Ligand classification

Organometallic compounds with metal-carbon bonds are formed by nearly all metallic elements, but those of transition metals show a diversity without parallel in main groups. Carbonyl has cyanide ligands are not considered organic, although they may also be present in organometallic compounds along with other π-acceptor ligands such as phosphines. *Table 8.5* shows a selection of the ligands found in organometallic compounds of transition metals, classified according to two properties given below:

(i) the **hapticity** is the number of carbon atoms bonded directly to the metal. With some ligands this can vary; for example, cyclopentadienyl can be $\eta^1 - C_5H_5$, $\eta^3 - C_5H_5$ or (most often) η^5 $-C_5H_5$ (pronounced 'monohapto', 'trihapto', etc.).

(ii) the **electron number** is the number of electrons the ligand contributes to the metal-carbon bonding. This is useful for applying the 18-electron (EAN) rule. Ligands are taken to be neutral species if they are known as stable anions (*e.g.*, C_5H_5, not $C_5H_5^-$). For ligands of variable hapticity the electron number often varies accordingly, but electron number is not always equal to the hapticity, as can be seen with η^1 ligands, where the electron number can vary from one to three.

Table 8.5. Some organic ligands, classified according to hapticity and electron number

Ligand name	Ligand formula	Hapticity	Electron number
Methyl, alkyl	CH_3, RCH_2	η^1	1
Alkylidene	R_2C	η^1	2
Alkylidyne	RC	η^1	3
Ethylene (ethane)	C_2H_4	η^2	2
Alkyl (propenyl)	CH_2CHCH_2	η^1	1*
		η^3	3
Cyclopentadienyl	C_0H_5	η^1	1*
		η^3	3*
		η^5	5
Benzene	C_0H_6	η^6	6

*Uncommon bonding arrangements.

Structure and Bonding

Alkyl ligands form metal-carbon σ bonds. Generally they occur in conjunction with other organic ligands or CO, but can be found on their own, as in tungsten hexamethyl (**1**), and in $[Ti(CH_2SiMe_3)_4]$ where the bulky groups are helpful in stabilizing the compound. Compounds with H attached to β carbons (the nomenclature being $M-C_\alpha-C_\beta-C_\gamma$) tend to be unstable to β-**hydride elimination** of an alkene fragment, discussed below. The surprising structure of (**1**), trigonal prismatic rather than octahedral as found in WCl_6, has been attributed to the orientation of d orbitals available for σ bonding. In an octahedral complex only two d orbitals (the e_g set) can be involved, but four in the trigonal prismatic structure. (Unlike WMe_6, WCl_6 also has some degree of W–Cl π bonding, which can involve the other d orbitals (t_{2g}) in octahedral geometry.

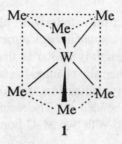

1

Alkylidene and alkylidyne ligands require metal-carbon π bonding in addition to σ. This is different, however, form π complexes where bonding involves only the π orbitals of alkene or aromatic ligands. Examples are the ethane complex $[(\eta^2 -C_2H_4)PtCl_3]^-$ **(2)** found in **Zeise's salt,** and the 'sandwich compound' **ferrocene** $[Fe(\eta^5 - C_5H_5)_2]$ **(3)**. The **Dewar-Chatt-Duncanson** model of bonding in ethene complexes is shown in *Fig.* And is analogous to the σ-donor-π-acceptor description of the bonding in carbonyl complexes (see Topic H9, *Fig.* 8.10). In the present case the 'σ-donor' character comes from the occupied bonding π MO of ethene (*Fig.* 8.10), back donation (*Fig.* 8.10) involving the empty π^* antibonding MO. The relative degrees of donor or acceptor behaviour depend on the compound.

$$\left[\begin{array}{c} \overset{Cl}{\underset{Cl}{\diagdown}} \\ Cl-Pt--\| \overset{CH_2}{\underset{CH_2}{}} \end{array} \right]^-$$

2

3

(a)   (b)

Fig. 8.7. Dewar-Chatt-Duncanson model for bonding in π complexes of C_2H_4.

With strongly electron-withdrawing alkenes such as C_2F_4 or $C_2(CN)_4$ there is a large amount of back donation, which weakens the C–C bond so that its length is similar to that of a single bond. The geometry of the ligand then also changes from the planar configuration associated with sp^2 hybridization, to a nonplanar from more characteristic of single-bonded sp^3. The result (4) can be viewed as a metallocyclic compound with two M–C bonds.

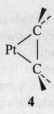

4

Bonding in sandwich compounds such as ferrocene arises through interaction of the delocalized π MOs of the ring with orbitals of the metal, and cannot be treated in a localized fashion. As in alkenes, both donor and acceptor interactions are involved. Other ligands such as CO can be present, as in the 'piano-stool' structure **5** or the metal-metal bonded dimer **6**.

5	**6**	**7**

The **18-electron rule** can be a useful guide to stable organometallic compounds, especially when π-acceptor ligands are present, although it has the limitations referred to in Topic H9. Compounds **3, 5** and **6** obey this rule, but **1** without π bonding ligands has an electron count of only 12. **Metallocenes** $[M(\eta^5-C_5H_5)_2]$ are known for the $3d$ series elements V–Ni, with 15–20 valence electrons, respectively. Ferrocene (M = Fe with 18 electrons) is by far the most stable of these, cobaltocene (M = Co with 19 electrons) being a very strong reducing agent that easily forms the 18-electron ion $[Co(\eta^5-C_5H_5)_2]^+$. Compounds with more than 18 valence electrons are uncommon, and thus one can understand the unusual structure of $[Fe(\eta^5-C_5H_5)(\eta^1-C_5H_5)(CO)_2]$ (**7**), as two pentahapto ligands would give an electron count of **22**. Reactions of organometallic compounds often involve 16-electron intermediates formed by the loss of one ligand (*e.g.,* CO) from an 18-electron parent compound.

Methods of Preparation

Methods of preparation for organometallic compounds are quite diverse but the following are generally useful.

(i) Reduction of metal salt in the presence of the ligand:

$$CrCl_3 + Al + 2C_6H_6 \rightarrow AlCl_3 + [Cr(\eta^6-C_6H_6)_2]$$

(ii) Reaction of transition metal salt with a main-group organometallic compound. C_5H_5 is often delivered as the sodium salt $Na^+(C_5H_5)^-$:

$$FeCl_2 + 2Na^+ + (C_5H_5)^- \rightarrow 2NaCl + [Fe(\eta^5-C_5H_5)_2]$$

In other cases a Grignard reagent or aluminum alkyl may often be used:

$$WCl_6 + 3Al_2(CH_3)_6 \rightarrow W(CH_3)_6 + 6AlCl(CH_3)_2]$$

(iii) **Metal vapour synthesis:** Vapourizing the metal (*e.g.,* by electron beam treating) helps by providing the sublimation energy required; metal atoms are then condensed in the presence of the ligand on the sides on the vessel, cooled in liquid nitrogen. This method is good for compounds that cannot be made by other routes, or ones stable only at low temperatures. For example,

$$Ti(g) + 2C_6H_6 \rightarrow [Ti(\eta^6 - C_6H_6)_2]$$

Insertion and Elimination

Among the many reactions of organometallic compounds, ones involving insertion and elimination of ligands are important in applications to synthesis and catalysis. An example of a **carbonyl insertion** is:

$$Mn(CO)_5CH_3 + CO \rightarrow Mn(CO)_5C(O)CH_3$$

where in a $Mn–CH_3$ bond is replaced by $Mn–C(O)–Ch_3$. The terminology is misleading as it is established by isotopic labelling that the incoming CO is not the one inserted. The first step is a reversible **alkyl migration** leading to a 16-electron intermediate

$$Mn(CO)_5CH_3 \leftrightarrow Mn(CO)_4–C(O)CH_3$$

which then picks up another CO molecule.

Many other unsaturated ligands can 'insert' into M–C or M–H bonds; for example, alkanes as in:

$$LnMH + CH_2 = CH_2 \rightarrow LnM–CH_2–CH_3$$

Such reactions are generally reversible, the backwards process leading to **elimination** of a ligand. The reverse of alkene insertion is the β-hydride elimination reaction referred to above.

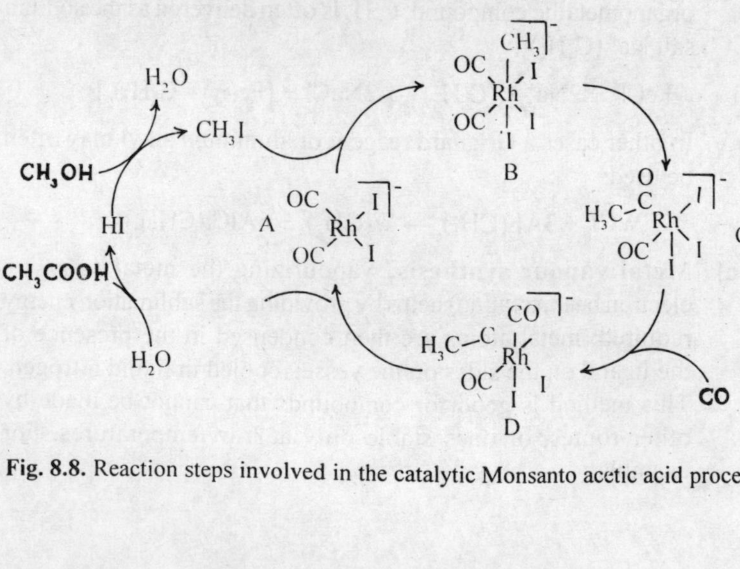

Fig. 8.8. Reaction steps involved in the catalytic Monsanto acetic acid process.

Organometallic compounds are used widely as homogeneous catalysts in the chemical industry (see Topic J5). For example, if the alkene insertion reaction continues with further alkene inserting into the M–C bond, it can form the basis for **catalytic alkene polymerization**. Other catalytic cycles may include **oxidative addition** and **reductive elimination** steps as described in Topic H9. *Figure* 8.8 shows the steps involved in the **Monsanto acetic acid** process, which performs the conversion

$$CH_3OH + CO \rightarrow CH_3CO_2H$$

In the catalytic cycle on the right hand side, the 16-electron species **A** undergoes oxidative addition of CH_3I to form **B**. carbonyl insertion then proceeds via **C** to give **D**, which regenerates **A** by reductive elimination of CH_3CoI. The organic steps on the left-hand side of *Fig.* 8.8 can be varied to give different overall reactions, for example, converting $CH_3CO_2CH_3$ into $(CH_3CO)_2O$.

9

Lanthanides and Actinides

9.1 Lanthanum and Lanthanides

Lanthanides are 14 elements following lanthanum (z = 57) in the periodic table. They involve the filling of 4f-orbitals. These f-orbitals belong to the shell third from the outermost shell. To denote lanthanides collectively the symbol Ln is generally used. Their electronic configurations are complex with electrons in 4f, 5d and 6s orbitals outside the Xe core. These are listed in Table 9.1.

Table 9.1. Electronic Configuration of Lanthanides

Element	Symbol	Atomic Number	Configuration
Lanthanum	La	57	$5d^1\ 6s^2$
Cerium	Ce	58	$4f^2\ 6s^2$
Praseodymium	Pr	59	$4f^3\ 6s^2$
Neodymium	Nd	60	$4f^4\ 6s^2$
Promethium	Pm	61	$4f^5\ 6s^2$
Samarium	Sm	62	$4f^6\ 6s^2$
Europium	Eu	63	$4f^7\ 6s2$
Gadolinium	Gd	64	$4f^7\ 5d^1\ 6s^2$
Terbium	Tb	65	$4f^9\ 6s^2$
Dysprosium	Dy	66	$4f^{10}\ 6s^2$
Holmium	Ho	67	$4f^{11}\ 6s^2$

Element	Symbol	Atomic Number	Configuration
Holmium	Ho	67	$4f^{11} 6s^2$
Erbium	Er	68	$4f^{12} 6s^2$
Thulium	Tm	69	$4f^{13} 6s^2$
Ytterbium	Yb	70	$4f^{14} 6s^2$
Lutetium	Lu	71	$4f^{14} 5d^1 6s^2$

Lanthanum, the first member of lanthanides has the configuration of $5d^1 6s^2$ and next member cerium, has $4f^2 6s^2$ while the next element praseodymium has the configuration $4f^3 6s^2$. Although lanthanum itself does not possess any $4f$ electrons, it is customary to include this element in the series. The electronic configurations of the elements with fully filled (f^{14}) and half-filled (f^7) f-orbitals are relatively more stable. The extra stability of half-filled orbitals is seen in the elements europium ($4f^7 6s^2$) and gadolinium ($4f^7 5d^1 6s^2$). The element ytterbium has fully-filled f-orbitals with the configuration $4f^{14} 6s^2$ and the extra electrons in lutetium goes in $5d$ orbitals ($4f^{14} 5d^1 6s^2$). So except for lanthanum, gadolinium and lutetium which have a single electron in $5d$ orbitals the lanthanides do not have electron in the $5d$ orbitals.

Lanthanides are silvery white metals having low tensile strengths. They are good conductors of heat and electricity. The first three ionisation energies are relatively low. The IE_1 and IE_2 values are quite comparable to those of alkaline earth metals particularly calcium.

Due to the low values of I.E., they are electropositive metals and their chemistry is dominated by Ln^{3+} state in solution and ionic solids.

The oxidation states +2 and +4 are found for some elements, following the trend in ionization energies across the series, which show pattern analogous to those found in configurations of p and d electrons. The third ionization energy rises from La to Eu (see Fig 9.1) and then drop occurs after the half-filled shell (Eu^{2+}, $4f^7$). The rise then continues to Yb, and drops at Lu because the $4f$ shell is filled and the electron ionized is in $5d$. Fourth ionization energies (which are substantially larger) show a similar pattern displaced by one element thus rising from Ce to Gd and falling to Tb.

Unlike the case with the d orbitals in the transition elements, spectra and magnetism associated with $4f$ orbitals in Ln^{3+} compounds are very similar to those found in free gas-phase ions. Ligand field and chemical bonding effects associated with incomplete $4f$ orbitals are very small and hardly detectable in chemical trends. The chemistry of all Ln^{3+} ions is therefore very similar and differentiated only by the gradual contraction in radius associated with increasing nuclear charge. The **lanthanide contraction** is also important for the transition elements of the $5d$ series.

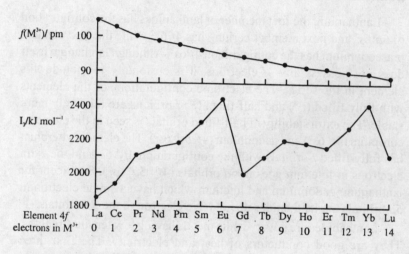

Fig. 9.1. Ionic radius of M^{3+}, third ionization energy I_3, and number of $4f$ electrons in M^{3+} for the elements La-Lu.

Promethium is a radioactive element with a half-life of 2.6 years and does not occur naturally. The other elements, known sometimes as the **rare earth elements**, are always found in association, principally in the minerals monazite ($LnPO_4$) and bastneasite ($LnCO_3F$). The electropositive and reactive elements can be obtained by reduction of $LnCl_3$ with Ca, and are sometimes used together as 'mischmetal'. Specialist applications of individual lanthanides depend on the spectroscopic properties of Ln^{3+} ions (*e.g.* Nd in lasers) and on the magnetic properties of some of the elements (*e.g.* Sm). The ions can be separated by ions-exchange chromatography from aqueous solution, using the variation of complexing properties across the series.

Oxidation State +3

The Ln^{3+} state is the most stable under normal conditions and all elements in the series. Halides LnX_3 and oxides Ln_2O_3 are known for all elements, as also an extensive range of oxo salts including mixed and hydrated compounds $Ln_2(SO_4)_3.3Na_2(SO_4).12H_2O$. Ionic radii vary from 104 pm (La^{3+}) to 86 pm (Lu^{3+}) and this relatively large size for 3+ ions (cf. Al^{3+} 53 pm) is associated with correspondingly high coordination numbers in solid compounds. LnF_3 compounds for earlier elements have nine-coordination, Ln_2O_3 are seven-coordinate. For later Ln elements the decrease in radius leads to changes in structure with reduction in coordination.

The **aqua Ln^{3+} ions** show slight acidity, which increases from La to Lu as the radius decreases but it still much less than for Al^{3+}. Strong complexes are formed with hard oxygen donor ligands, and especially chelating ones such as EDTA or β-diketonates (L–L = $[RC(O)CHC(O)R]^-$**1**), which give eight-coordinate complexes $[Ln(L–L)]^-$. Complex strengths generally increase across the series as the radius decreases and this may be used to separate a mixture of Ln^{3+} ions. For example, in an ion-exchange chromatography column with a complexing agent present in aqueous, the earlier lanthanides, which are less strongly complexed, are retained preferentially on the column and elute more slowly.

The organometallic chemistry of lanthanides is much more limited than in the *d* block. Compounds such as $(C_5H_5)_3Ln$ and $(C_5H_5)_2LnX$ (X = Cl, H, etc.) have more ionic character than for transition elements, and compounds with neutral ligands such as CO are not stable. Some interesting chemistry has, however, been found with compounds such as $(C_5(CH_3)_5)_2LuH$ where a bulky ligand is combined with a small lanthanide. For example, the **methane activation** reaction

$$(C_5(CH_3)_5)_2LuH + CH_4 \rightarrow (C_5(CH_3)_5)_2LuCH_3 + H_2$$

occurs under mild conditions in solution.

Other Oxidation States

According to the ionic model the relative stability of Ln^{2+} and Ln^{3+} compounds in determined by a balance between the third ionization energy (I_3) of the lanthanide, and the difference of lattice (or solvation) energies associated with the two ions. The I_3 value for lanthanides is small enough that most Ln^{2+} compounds are unstable with respect to disproportionation to Ln and Ln^{3+}. The exceptions are of two kinds. For Sm, Eu and Tb, I_3 is large enough to stabilize a number of compounds such as SmO, EuF_2 and $YbCl_2$. The aqueous Ln^{2+} ions are strongly reducing, especially so for Sm and Yb. On the other hand, compounds with large anions have small lattice energies and so disproportionation is less favourable. Thus LnS and LnI_2 are known for all Ln. Many of these compounds are metallic in appearance and highly conducting, which suggests an unusual electron configuration as $4f$ orbitals on one atom cannot overlap sufficiently with orbitals on other atoms to forms bands. A formulation such as $(Ln^{3+})(S^{2-})(e^-)$ is sometimes given implying a $(4f)^n$ configuration appropriate to Ln^{3+} with one electron delocalised in a band (formed probably from overlapping $5d$ orbitals). For compounds of Sm, Eu and Yb this peculiarity disappears, and, for examples, EuS and YbI_2 are not metallic but have 'normal' Ln^{2+} ions.

Ln^{4+} compounds are known only for elements with the lowest I_4 values. Ce^{4+} is known in aqueous solution and forms many compounds such as CeO_2. Pr^{4+} and Tb^{4+} are more strongly oxidizing, giving fluorides LnF_4, and being present together with Ln^{3+} in mixed-valency oxides such as Pr_6O_{11} (which is actually non-stoichiometric).

9.2 Actinium and the Actinides

The series of elements involving the fillings of $5f$-orbitals is called actinide series. They follow Ac (89) and include elements from Th (90) and Lw (103). Their electronic configuration is shown in Table 9.2.

Table 9.2. Electronic Configuration of Actinides

Element	Symbol	Atomic Number	Configuration
Actinium	Ac	89	$6d^1\,7s^2$
Thorium	Th	90	$6d^2\,7s^2$
Protactinium	Pa	91	$5f^2\,6d^1\,7s^2$
Uranium	U	92	$5f^3\,6d^1\,7s^2$
Neptunium	Np	93	$5f^4\,6d^1\,7s^2$
Plutonium	Pu	94	$5f^6\,7s^2$
Americium	Am	95	$5f^7\,7s^2$
Curium	Cm	96	$5f^7\,6d^1\,7s^2$
Berkelium	Bk	97	$5f^8\,6d^1\,7s^2$
Californium	Cf	98	$5f^{10}\,7s^2$
Einsteinium	Es	99	$5f^{11}\,7s^2$
Fermium	Fm	100	$5f^{12}\,7s^2$
Mendelevium	Md	101	$5f^{13}\,7s^2$
Nobelium	No	102	$5f^{14}\,7s^2$
Lawrencium	Lr	103	$5f^{14}\,6d^1\,7s^2$

The chemistry of **actinides** is more complicated due to the existence of greater range of oxidation states for these metals. Moreover, all these metals are radioactive and therefore, their accessibility for laboratory investigations is limited. The elements beyond uranium are all man-made elements and are made by nuclear-chemical methods.

Early actinides show a variety of oxidation states. The +6 state is common for uranium (U). Later actinides are more similar to lanthanides, with +3 state being common.

Nuclear Properties

As already stated all the activities are radioactive. The following table (Table 9.2) lists their longest-lived isotopes.

The progressively shorter half-lives reflect the decreasing stability of heavy nuclei, resulting from the changing balance between the attractive strong interaction and the repulsive Coulomb forces. Most actinide nuclei undergo α **decay** by emitting. He, but for heavier elements **spontaneous fission** into two fragments is an increasingly important alternative decay route.

Table 9.2. Longest-lived isotopes of actinides

Atomic no.	Element	Isotope	Half-life
89	Actinium	^{227}Ac	21.77 years
90	Thorium	^{232}Th	1.40×10^{10} years
91	Protactinium	^{231}Pa	3.28×10^4 years
92	Uranium	^{235}U	7.04×10^8 years
		^{238}U	4.47×10^9 years
93	Neptinium	^{237}Np	2.14×10^6 years
94	Plutonium	^{244}Pu	8.26×10^7 years
95	Americium	^{243}Am	7370 years
96	Curium	^{247}Cm	1.65×10^7 years
97	Berkelium	^{247}Bk	1380 years
98	Californium	^{251}Cf	898 years
99	Einsteinium	^{253}Es	20.5 days
100	Fermium	^{257}Fm	100.5 days
101	Mendelevium	^{257}Md	5.2 h
102	Nobelium	^{259}No	1.0 h
103	Lawrencium	^{256}Lr	28 s

Only thorium and uranium have half-lives long enough to survive since the formation of the Earth. Thorium is found together with lanthanides in the phosphate mineral monazite ($LnPO_4$), and uranium occurs as pitchblende U_3O_3 and carnotite $K_2(UO_2)_2(VO_4)_2.3H_2O$. Uranium is principally used as a nuclear fuel, as the isotope ^{235}U undergoes neutron-induced fission, the nucleus splitting into two smaller fragments together with more neutrons, which can thus initiate a chain reaction. The energy liberated (about 2×10^{10} kJ mol^{-1}) is vastly greater than that obtainable from chemical reactions.

^{232}Th, ^{235}U and ^{238}U are the first members of **radioactive decay series**, forming other radioactive elements with atomic numbers 84–91, which are therefore present in small amounts in thorium and unranium. Each series ends with a different stable isotope of lead (^{208}Pb, ^{207}Pb and ^{306}Pb, respectively, and the proportions of these presents in natural lead samples varies detectably. This variation can be used to give geological information, including an estimate of the age of the Earth.

Transuranium elements beyond U do not occur naturally on Earth but can be made artificially. The neutron irradiation of ^{238}U in nuclear reactors produces ^{239}U, which rapidly undergoes β decay to ^{239}NP and thence to ^{239}Pu. Further neutron irradiation produces heavier actinides in progressively smaller amounts, up to Fm. The remaining elements Md, No and Lr cannot be obtained in this way but have been produced in exceedingly small quantities by bombardment of lighter actinides with nuclei such as ^{4}He and ^{12}C using particle accelerators. (Note that the longest-lived isotopes listed in *Table 9.2* are not necessarily the ones most easily made.) Similar methods have been used to make **transactinide elements** with atomic number up to 110, presumably forming part of $6d$ transition series. However, the very small quantities made (often a few atoms only) and their very short half-lives maker chemical studies almost impossible.

Chemical Properties

Unlike the $4f$ orbitals in the lanthanides, the $5f$ orbitals in the earlier actinide elements are more expanded and so can be engaged in chemical bonding. This leads to a pattern of chemistry more analogous to that found in the d block, with the possibility of variable oxidation states up to the maximum possible determined by the number of valence electrons. Most thorium compounds contain Th^{IV} (*e.g.* ThO_2) and with uranium the states from +3 to +6 can be formed. UO_2 is frequently nonstoichiometric, and the natural mineral U_3O_8 probably contains U^{IV} and U^{VI}. **Uranium hexafluoride** is made industrially using CIF_3 as a fluorinating agent

$$U(s) + 3CIF_3(g) \rightarrow UF_6(I) + 3CIF(g)$$

Being volatile, it is used to separate the isotopes ^{235}U and ^{238}U for nuclear fuel applications. Many other U^{VI} compounds contain the **Uranyl ion** UO^{2+}_2, a linear unit with bonding involving both $5f$ and $6d$ orbitals: examples include the mineral carnotite (see above) and $Cs_2[UO_2Cl_4]$ where uranyl is complexed to four chloride ions.

The maximum attainable oxidation state in the series is +7, in the mixed oxides Li_5AnO_6 (An = Np, Pu). With increasing atomic number high oxidation states become more strongly oxidizing, as in the d block. This trend is illustrated in Fig. 9.2.

Figure 9.2, which shows a Frost diagram with the oxidation states of some actinides found in aqueous solution. The oxocations AnO^+_2 and AnO^{2+}_2 are characteristic for An^V and An^{VI} with An = U, Np, Pu and Am, but the slopes of the lines in the diagram show their increasingly strong oxidizing character. Complex solution equilibria are possible: with Pu, for example, all states from +3 to +6 can be present simultaneously. The different redox stability of U and Pu is important in **nuclear fuel reprocessing,** one function of which is to separate unused uranium from ^{239}Pu, which is itself used as a nuclear fuel. Dissolving the spent fuel elements in aqueous HNO_3 gives Pu^{VI} and U^{VI}. Subsequent separation steps then depend on differences in complexing power and solubility of these ions.

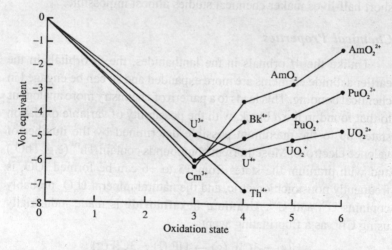

Fig. 9.2. Frost diagram showing the oxidation states of some actinides in aqueous solution at pH = 0.

The **organometallic chemistry** is much less extensive than that of the d block (see Topic H10), and differs from that of the lanthanides by virtue of the large size of the early actinides, and their wide range of accessible oxidation states. Uranium has been much more investigated than other elements. Typical compounds include the cyclopentadienyl (Cp = η^5–C_5H_5) compounds [$AnCp_3$], [$AnCp_4$] and mixed Cp-halide, such as [$AnCp_3Cl$]. Particularly interesting is the sandwich compound [U(η^8–C_8H_8)$_2$] with two planar cyclooctatetraene rings known as **uranocene**; analogs are formed with neighbouring actinides. Although formally they can be regarded as compounds of An^{4+} with the aromatic 10 π electron ring [C_8H_8]$^{2-}$ (see Topic C6] there is some covalent bonding involving actinide $5f$ and $6d$ orbitals.

Later actinides show a much more restricted range of oxidation states, and are more similar to the lanthanides. The +4 state is found in AnO_2 and AnF_4 as far as Cf. It becomes progressively more oxidizing for later elements, but with a break at Bk^{4+} (which is more easily formed than Cm^{4+} or Cf^{4+}) following the half-filled $5f$ shell and so analogous to the occurrence of Tb^{4+} in the lanthanides. From Am to Md the +3 state is most stable in solid compounds and aqueous solution. Near the end of the series, however, the +2 state appears more stable than in the lanthanides and is the normal one for No. This difference must reflect a different balance of ionization energies and lattice or solvation energies, but the data required to understand it in detail are not available, with only a few atoms available, and with very short half-lives, chemical investigations of later actinides depend on **tracer techniques** using a stable element of presumed similar chemical behaviour to act as a carrier. For example, the presence of No^{2+} can be inferred from its precipitation (and subsequent detection by its radioactivity) along with Ba^{2+} and $BaSO_4$ under conditions where other oxidation states form soluble compounds.